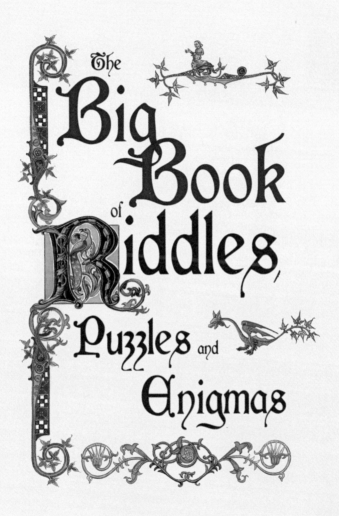

The Big Book of Riddles, Puzzles and Enigmas

This edition published in 2008 by Carlton Books Limited
20 Mortimer Street
London W1T 3JW

Copyright © Marabout 2007

English translation by Tom Clegg

ISBN 978-1-84732-118-3

Printed in China

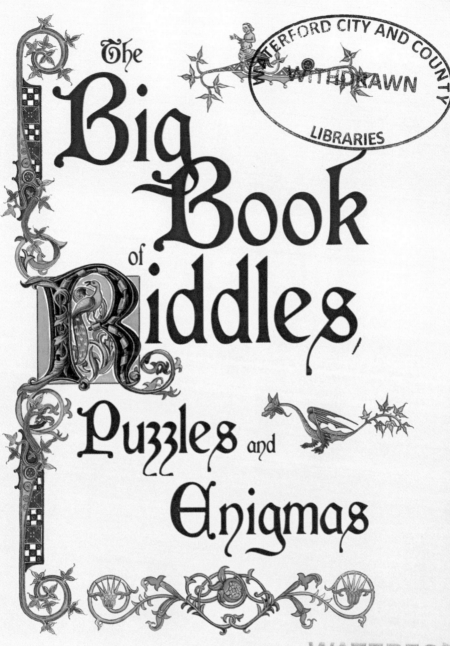

The Big Book of Riddles, Puzzles and Enigmas

Fabrice Mazza

Sylvain Lhullier

Illustrations by Ivan Sigg

CARLTON BOOKS

ONTENTS

	Riddle	Solution

INTRODUCTION - TO THE READER

Is there anyone out there who has never enjoyed challenging the minds of friends or acquaintances with a brain-teasing enigma - especially one that may leave them momentarily at a complete loss for the answer?

In fact, there is an ages old tradition of such enigmas that dates back millennia. They have been transmitted, transformed and enriched over the years at countless firesides, as well as through myths, literature and in our times, Internet.

I have selected the best and most amusing enigmas of this type, ones that require inventiveness, shrewdness and wisdom to solve.

Because the pleasure of a good enigma resides therein: the seeking… But also in finding - and finding on your own - path to the solution. No two people arrive at the solution in the same way, and therein lies the interest in sharing these puzzles with your friends. So I urge you, the reader, not to look at the answers except in case of imminent danger of cerebral meltdown.

This book is intended to perpetuate the tradition of enigmas: now it is up to you to transmit them, transform them and further enrich them.

Happy reading, and happy hunting!

Fabrice Mazza

RIDDLES

PART ONE

 OVE POTION

Merlin must prepare a love potion for King Arthur. According to his book of magic spells, he needs 4 fluid ounces of oil of toad.

   To measure volumes, the wizard only has two unmarked jars, one of them containing 5 fl oz, the other 3 fl oz.

How can he measure 4 dl?

Solution on page 224

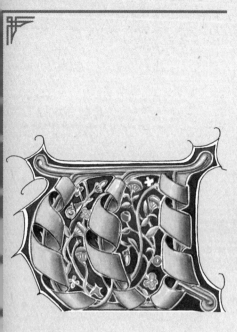ATER IN THE WINE

You have two perfectly identical mugs; one contains 15 fl oz of wine, the other 15 fl oz of water.

You take a spoonful from the water mug and empty it into the mug of wine before mixing it thoroughly.

Next, you fill the same spoon from this second mug and empty it into the first. So once again, you have 15 fl oz of liquid in each mug.

Which of them has more water in the wine, or wine in the water?

Solution on page 225

 YCLING RACE

During a Draisine race, Roland passes the rider in second place, then, as he approaches the finishing line, he is himself passed by two rivals on their wooden push bikes. In what place does he finish?

Solution on page 226

ELLS

Quasimodo, the bell ringer of Notre-Dame cathedral in Paris, takes three seconds to ring four o'clock.

How long does it take him to ring midday?

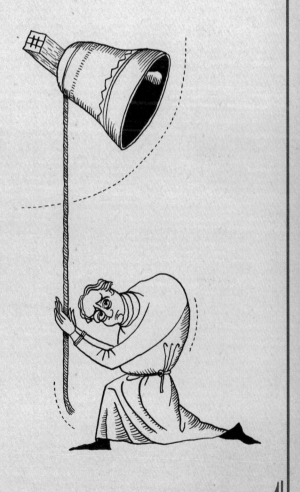

Solution on page 227

RIANGLE TEASER

Fill in this triangle so that the number inscribed in each space is equal to the sum of the two numbers inscribed in the two spaces immediately below it.

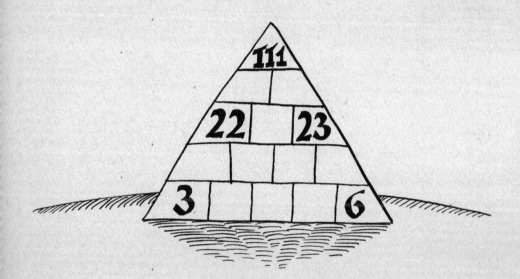

BRAIN-TEASER

Can you place the five letters A, B, C, D, and E within this square so that no letter is repeated in the same row, or in the same column, or diagonally?

Solution on page 229

KINSHIP BOND

You ask yourself this:

"I am a man. If the son of this other man is the father of my son, what is the bond of kinship between this man and myself?"

Solution on page 230

 UM OF 1 TO 100

Calculate the sum of the first one hundred whole numbers: 1 + 2 + 3 + ... + 99 + 100 = ?

Solution on page 231

 PLACE OF THEIR OWN

A copyist proposes rearranging seating in the Illuminations Hall.

Lady Clarissa wants to sit behind Friar Stephen, but the latter won't hear of it: it will be he who sits behind Lady Clarissa!

How do they resolve the problem?

Solution on page 232

ENTAL CALCULATION

Divide 30 by ½ then add 20 to the result.
What number do you get?

 UT-UP SQUARE

How can you turn the cross on this armour into a square with just two scissor cuts, knowing that you can move the pieces about?

Solution on page 234

ISH

This fish composed of eight matches is swimming to the right.
By shifting three matches, make it swim to the left.

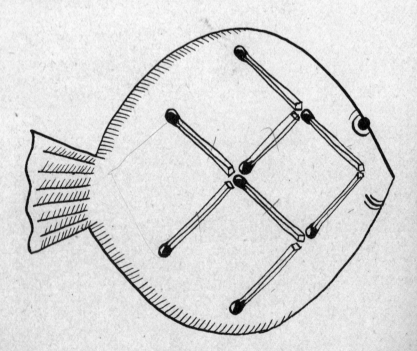

Solution on page 235

ATCH TRIANGLES 1

How can the carpenter's apprentice at the building site in Catfisher
Street create eight equilateral trangles with six matches?

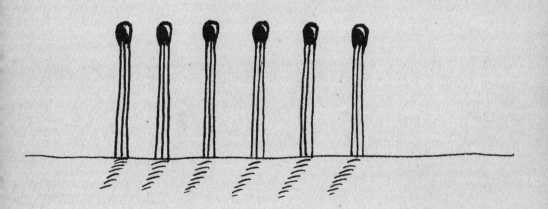

HE MONK AND THE MOUNTAIN

As penitence for breaking silence during supper, a monk has to climb a mountain. He leaves in the morning at 9am and arrives at the summit by 12noon. He rests overnight, sleeping under the stars, and starts back down at 9am the next morning. Following the same path in reverse, he arrives at the bottom by 11am. Is there any point along this route where he finds himself in the same place at the same time on both days?

How can you prove the existence or non-existence of such a point?

Solution on page 237

36

PILLS

Lady Fredegonde's apothecary prescribes eight pills, to be taken one at a time every quarter of an hour. How much time will have passed by the time she finishes taking her pills?

Solution on page 238

HIELD TRIANGLES

Have a look at these two shields:

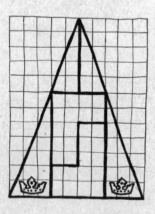 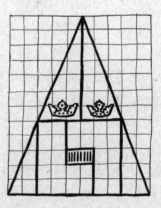

The parts of the first shield have been rearranged to form the
second, to which two small squares have had to be added.
How do you explain the presence of these squares, shown as
a striped rectangle?

Hint 1
Certain points, which seem to be aligned, are not, in fact.

Hint 2
The two shields are not triangles.

Solution on page 239

ARALLELEPIPED

Is segment AB longer than segment BC?

Solution on page 240

1 = 2 ?

Let's say a = 1, b = 1

a = b [1] Obviously!

a × a = a × b [2]

Multiply both sides of the equation by a.

a × a - b × b = a × b - b × b [3]

Subtract b × b from both sides.

a × a + a × b - a × b - b × b = b × (a - b) [4]

Add 0 = a × b - a × b on the left; we factorize b on the right.

a × (a + b) - b × (a + b) = b (a - b) [5]

Factorize twice (a and b) on the left.

(a + b) × (a - b) = b × (a - b) [6]

Factorize (a +b) on the left.

a + b = b [7]

Simplify.

2 = 1 [8]

And cry foul... Yes, but where is the error?

Solution on page 241

BRACADABRA

Starting with the letter A at the top of the triangle and reading downwards, always moving to an adjoining letter, how many ways are there of spelling out the word ABRACADABRA?

Solution on page 242

WO RESULTS FOR THE SAME NUMBER?

Let a = 0.99999999999999999... (to infinity)
Note: there is a number with infinite decimal places - think of the famous √2.
So let us take a, the number whose integral part is 0 and whose decimal part is an infinite series of 9s.

a = 0.99999999999999... [1] By definition.
10 x a = 9.99999999999999... [2] Multiply by 10.
10 x a = 9 + 0.9999999999999... [3]
Separate the integral and decimal parts on the right side of the equation.
10 x a = 9 + a [4] By definition.
10 x a - a = 9 [5]. Subtract a from both sides.
9 x a = 9 [6] Using the fact that 10 - 1 = 9.
a = 1 [7] Divide both sides by 9.

Question: Is it then true that 1 = 0.99999999999999999...?

Solution on page 243

ECHANICAL
ALARM CLOCK

You need to wake up early tomorrow morning so you use your mechanical alarm clock (with hour and minute hands) because it has a loud ring. You set it to ring at 10am and you go to sleep at 9pm. How long will you sleep?

Solution on page 244

ROUBADOUR

A troubadour holding three objects (a ball, a hat and a bowling pin) arrives at a bridge. The bridgekeeper warns him, 'The bridge won't bear more than your weight plus a maximum of two objects, and it's not possible to throw the objects over to the far side.'

The troubadour nevertheless manages to get to the other side carrying his three objects in a single crossing.

How does he do it?

Solution on page 245

OGICAL SERIES 1

Complete this series:

o t t f f s s

LAZIERS

Two master glaziers are competing to make the stained glass
windows for Chartres cathedral. To decide which one will be
awarded the job, the archbishop issues them with the following
challenge:

'Here is a square of glass with sides measuring 12 inches and
a ring with a diameter of 2½ inches. He who manages to cut the
glass into four equal pieces so that they can slip through the ring
without breaking will be given the task.'

How should they proceed given that each has a diamond allowing them to cut the glass in any direction?

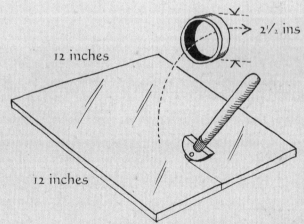

12 inches

12 inches

2½ ins

HIELD OF NAILS

How can this shield be divided into four exactly equal zones, each containing the same number of nails?

Solution on page 248

 UESTION OF AGE

A master asks his pupil:

'I am four times as old as you were when I was the same age as you are now. I am forty years old, how old are you?'

Solution on page 249

HE GUARDS' HALL

In the Guards' Hall, six hundred men wait to be sent off to war. Among them, 5% have one weapon. Among the remaining 95%, half of them bear two weapons, while the others have none. How many weapons are there in total within the Guards' Hall?

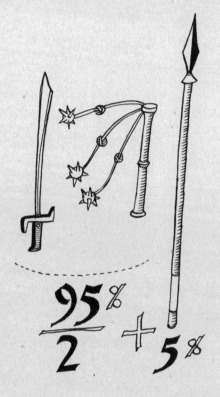

$$\frac{95\%}{2} + 5\%$$

ATCH TRIANGLES 2

At the cathedral building site, a journeyman wonders, during his break, how he might form four equilateral triangles with six matches.

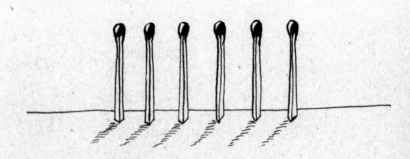

Solution on page 251

 ORK

Here is a fork formed by four matches and containing marbles:

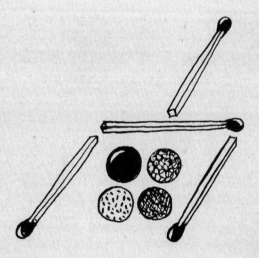

By shifting two matches, the fork has exactly the same shape, but the marbles are now outside it. Which matches should be moved to achieve this?

SYMBOLS

a	2	a				
	e		g	e		
	8	g		h		8
2		h		3	3	
8	h		2	e	e	
	a	g				2
	3	h	g	3		
	a			8		

Divide this square into four parts equal in size and in such a way that each part contains seven different symbols.

Solution on page 253

NINE POINTS

Let's assume we have a grid of nine points that looks like this:

Looking at his plan, the architect of the crypt wonders how he can connect these points by drawing four straight lines without lifting his pen… Can you help him?

Solution on page 254

INGLE FILE

King Arthur set a challenge for four of the Knights of the
Round Table:

'I'm going to put you in a line, and you musn't turn around or
communicate with one another.'

A tapestry is placed between Lancelot and the others. Lancelot
and Galahad can't see any of the other three.

Percival can see Galahad, and Gawain can see Percival and
Galahad.

'I have here four helmets, two of them with a white feather on top, two with a black feather. Close your eyes while I place them on your heads. If one of you can tell me the colour of the feather on top of his own helmet, that knight will win Excalibur!'

They open their eyes, and after a few moments' reflection, one of the four knights finds the correct answer.

Which knight won Excalibur? And how did he know the colour of the feather on the top of his helmet?

Solution on page 255

A WOLF, A GOAT AND A CABBAGE

Accompanied by a wolf, a goat, and a cabbage, you must cross a river in order to get home. Unfortunately, you have a tiny boat which only permits you to transport a single load at a time. Therefore, during each trip, you must leave two unguarded on the riverbank while making the crossing. How will you manage to get all of them safely across, without one of them being eaten (the wolf will eat the goat, and the goat will eat the cabbage)?

Solution on page 256

 UBTRACTION

How many times can you subtract 6 from 36?

$$36 - 6$$

ANUSCRIPT

A cleric must number the pages of a manuscript from 1 to 100.
How many times will he inscribe the figure 9?

Solution on page 258

 ANDICAPS

You are blind, deaf and dumb. How many senses do you still possess?

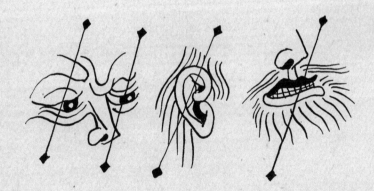

Solution on page 259

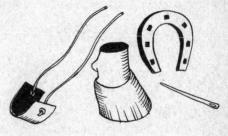

ALL

Two peasant boys are playing with a ball made of wicker. One of them drops the ball into a cylindrical hole sunk 12 ins deep into the ground. The hole's diameter is a fraction of an inch greater than that of the ball. How can this clumsy boy recover the ball, knowing that the only objects available to him are:

- a sling,
- a horse's hoof,
- an embroidering needle,
- a horseshoe.

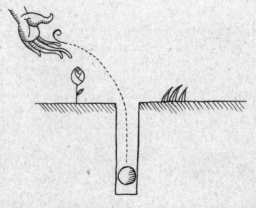

Solution on page 260

TANDARD

Here is a battle standard composed of eight squares arranged in the following manner:

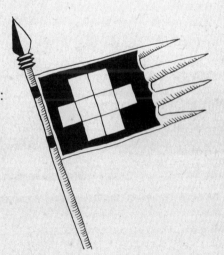

Place each of the numbers running from 1 to 8 in the squares of the standard so than none of the numbers is in contact on any side or diagonally with another number that directly precedes it or follows it.

Hint:
Two of the numbers have a characteristic that is distinct from the other six.

Solution on page 261

RIANGLE AND SUMS

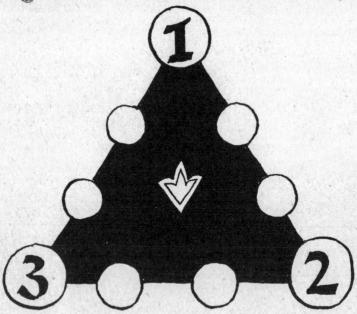

Place two numbers from 4 to 9 on each side of this triangle so that the sum of each side is equal to 17.

Be careful! You can only use each number once (and 1, 2, and 3 are already in place).

Solution on page 262

PRECIOUS STONES

King Louis the Large wants to have a crown made with precious stones. He knows from an informer that one of the nine stones presented to him by the merchant is a fake. But the merchant won't admit to this. The king also knows that each of the stones weighs the same, except the fake, which is slightly heavier. So, he asks the merchant to bring out his scales and manages to find the false stone with just two weighings.

How does he manage this?

Solution on page 263

 INE LEVEL

Two drunkards find a cask of wine without a lid, perfectly symmetrical, and roughly half full of wine. One of the men asserts that the level of wine is actually more than half of the cask, while the other claims that it is less.

How can they determine which of them is right, knowing that they have neither a measuring instrument of any sort, nor any container?

Solution on page 264

 TRANGE EQUIVALENCE

In what period of history might this equivalence be said to be true?

$$31_{OCT} = 25_{DEC}$$

UT-UP

Cut this headdress up into four superimposable parts.

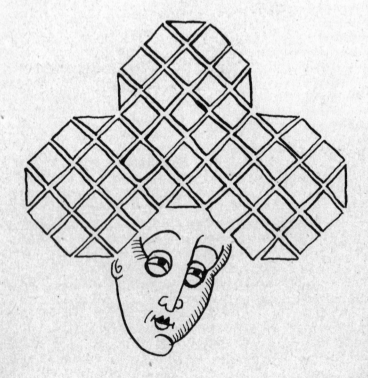

Solution on page 266

ATCHES 1

The master glazier is planning the composition of his stained glass window with the help of some matches. His problem is the following: how can he obtain three squares from this drawing by removing eight matches?

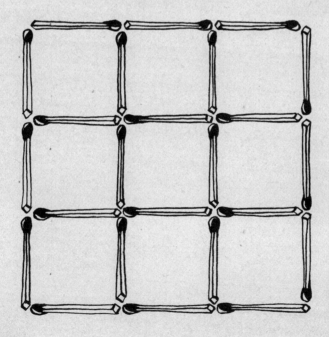

ONNECTIONS

Here are two houses, M1 and M2.

You need to connect them to electricity (A), gas (B), and water (C), knowing that:

- each of these three services (A, B, and C) must be connected to each of the two houses (M1 and M2);

- the lines must not touch or cross, but they can be long and curvy.

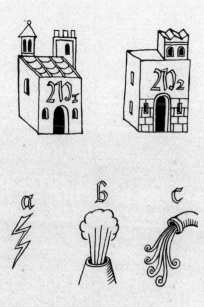

Solution on page 268

PART TWO

ATCHES 2

How does one obtain four identical squares that touch one another from these five squares, by moving only three matches?

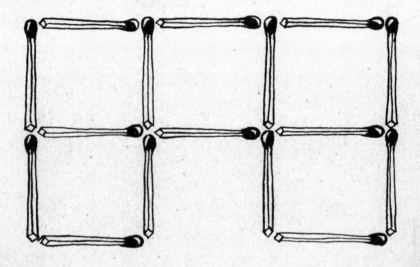

Solution on page 269

ILL IN THE HEAD

Do the following calculation in your head:

The initial amount is 1 million.
Divide it by 4.
Divide the result by 5.
Divide the result by 2.
Divide the result by 20.
Subtract 50.
Divide by 3 then by 8.
Subtract 1.
Divide the result by 7.
Add 2.
Divide by 3.
Add 2.
Lastly, divide by 5.

What result do you obtain?

AKE 24 WITH 5, 5, 5 AND 1

How to do you get 24 by using each of the numbers 5, 5, 5, and 1? The only operations allowed are addition, subtraction, multiplication and division.

PREDICTION

Nostradamus announced the following:

'On Wednesday 2 February 2000, a world event will take place for the first time in over a thousand years, not seen since 28 August 888.'

What could he have meant?

Solution on page 272

TOURNAMENT

On your way to a tournament, you meet six knights, each accompanied by six squires. Each squire leads two horses by the reins, and on each horse are seated two young children.

How many people and animals are going to the tournament?

Solution on page 273

E WHO LOSES, WINS

During a tournament, two knights are tied for first place.

To decide the winner, the king tells them:

'Look at that tower over there on the horizon. The one whose horse arrives last at this tower will be the winner of the tournament.'

Upon hearing this, the two knights rush to the stables, where each of them quickly mounts a horse and heads for the tower at full gallop!

How do you explain the apparently illogical behaviour on the part of the two knights?

Solution on page 274

 EADDRESS

In a room without any light are three black headdresses and two white ones.

Three ladies of the court are allowed entry, the last of whom is blind. Each of them takes a headdress at random and places it on her head. The two remaining headdresses are removed.

Candles are lit and each lady is asked whether she is capable of guessing the colour of her headdress.

The first lady looks at the two others and says, 'NO.'

The second lady also looks at the two others and answers, 'NO.'

The third, despite being blind, answers, 'YES.'

How has this blind lady correctly guessed the colour of her headdress?

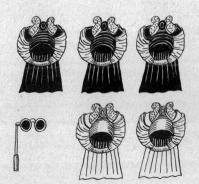

Solution on page 275

ROMAN NUMERAL EQUATION 1

Look at this equation:

What do you need to do, without modifying the terms, to make this equation valid?

Solution on page 276

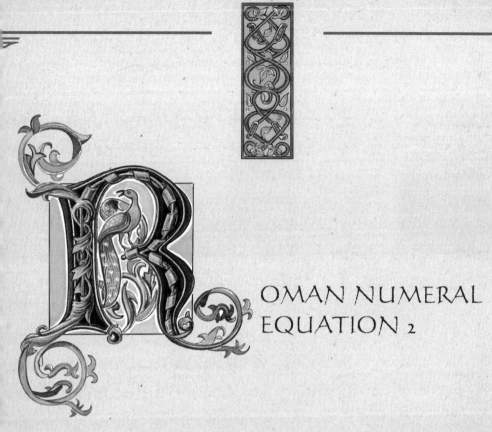

ROMAN NUMERAL EQUATION 2

Here is another strange equation:

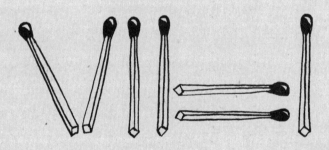

What do you need to do, by moving just one match, to make this equation valid (other than simply crossing the '=' sign to make '≠')?

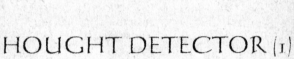# HOUGHT DETECTOR (1)

Think of a number composed of two figures. From this number, subtract each of the two figures that compose it. Lastly, in the table opposite, find the symbol that corresponds to the result:

99 n	98 o	97 R	96 b	95 o	94 T	93 l	92 ^	91 T	90 _
89 z	88 S	87 ^	86 M	85 m	84 b	83 {	82]	81 S	80 N
79 l	78 O	77 U	76 S	75 u	74 l	73 R	72 S	71 u	70 m
69 6	68 u	67 o	66 S	65 M	64 o	63 S	62 ^	61]	60 {
59 h	58 d	57 f	56 u	55 u	54 S	53 U	52 M	51 i	50 o
49 i	48 l	47 x	46 h	45 S	44 n	43 l	42 n	41 N	40 b
39 ^	38 m	37 v	36 S	35 6	34 6	33 z	32 S	31 l	30 ^
29 ^	28 v	27 S	26 U	25 O	24 z	23 x	22 {	21 v	20 U
19 b	18 S	17 o	16 l	15 d	14 o	13 T	12 f	11 l	10 b
9 S	8 l	7 T	6 d	5 T	4 ^	3 S	2 o	1 i	0 S

Now check the solution.

Solution on page 278

HOUGHT DETECTOR (2)

Choose a number from 1 to 10.

Multiply it by 2.

Add 8.

Divide the result obtained by 2.

Lastly, subtract the number you chose at the beginning and find the letter corresponding to that number in the list of cards below.

Now think of the name of a country starting with this letter.

Now think of a big animal whose name starts with the second letter of the name of this country.

Solution on page 279

ATCH SQUARE

Four matches are arranged in a cross:

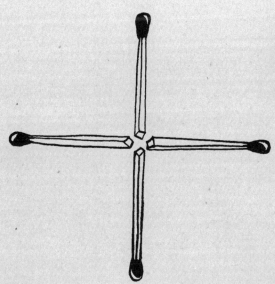

How can you obtain a square by moving just a single match?

Solution on page 280

IVE SQUARES

A troubadour at the fair has created a figure formed by five squares.

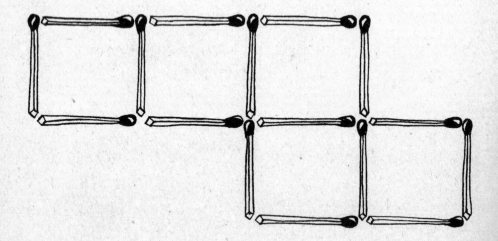

How does he form four squares of the same size by moving just two matches?

Solution on page 281

PATHS

Draw lines linking dwellings 1 to 1, 2 to 2 and 3 to 3, without crossing lines or going outside the frame of this picture.

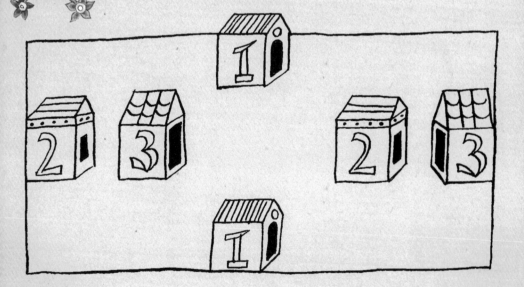

Solution on page 282

SOLATION

At the hospital, a patient has come down with the plague.

To prevent it from spreading, it's been decided that the patients in the common ward should be separated with the help of two screens, each in the form of a square, which can be of any size.

How should these two square screens be placed in order to isolate each patient?

Solution on page 283

AIGHT QUEENS

How can eight queens be arranged on a chessboard so that none of them are in 'check' from another queen.

Reminder: queens can move in straight lines or diagonally.

Solution on page 284

 OUR QUEENS AND A
BISHOP

On a chessboard, how can four queens and a bishop be placed so
that the opposing king is always in check, whatever his position?
   Reminder: queens can move in straight lines or diagonally,
bishops move diagonally.

	a	b	c	d	e	f	g	h
8								
7								
6								
5								
4								
3								
2								
1								

Solution on page 285

ICIOUS CIRCLE

Write out the missing figure in letters, while preserving the coherence of the sentence.

In this circle the "r" is present ... times

Solution on page 286

CCURRENCES

King Dagobert is absent-minded, and has forgotten the code for the strongbox in which he keeps his royal regalia.

He goes to see Saint Éloi, his treasurer, to whom he remembers having confided something that will jog his memory, just in case. The saint hands him a parchment which reads:

'To recover the code for the strongbox, you need to replace the blanks in the following sentence with numbers; in such a way that the sentence shall remain coherent (the inserted numbers also being counted). The ten inserted numbers, in order, shall provide the code.'

Here is the sentence:

'In this sentence, the number of occurrences of 0 is _, of 1 is _, of 2 is _, of 3 is _, of 4 is _, of 5 is _, of 6 is _, of 7 is _, of 8 is _, and of 9 is _.'

What is the code King Dagobert must apply in order to open the strongbox and retrieve his crown?

Solution on page 287

 ARPET

Charlemagne's bedchamber measures 12 by 9 yards. In the middle is a rectangular fireplace 8 yards long and 1 yard wide. The chamber thus has a usable surface of 100 square yards (12 × 9 - 8 × 1) = 100). It is represented by the figure below:

To make it more comfortable, the Emperor wants to cover the floor with a carpet brought from the Orient, measuring 10 × 10 yds.

How can the entire floor be covered with this carpet, by cutting it into two superimposable pieces of the same size?

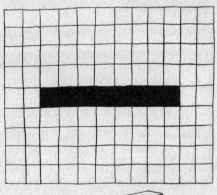

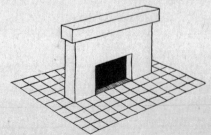

Solution on page 288

VALON

Avalon is a square island surrounded by a river 4 yards wide. You have two boards 3.90 yards long and several inches wide. How can you arrange them to make a stable bridge allowing you to cross over to the legendary isle?

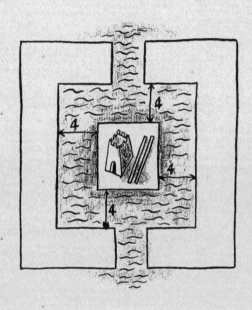

Solution on page 289

OGICAL SERIES 2

Complete this series:

EOEREX...

Solution on page 290

OGICAL SERIES 3

Complete this series:

1 (2,3) 2 (5,6) 4 (11,30) 26 (?,?) ?

URDEROUS ITINERARY

A prison is composed of sixteen cells.

The prisoner in the upper left-hand cell has the key to the lower right-hand cell.

Having decided to escape, he breaks through the wall to the neighbouring cell and kills the prisoner within, leaving the body in place. He goes through all of the cells, killing all of the prisoners, but never returns to a cell where there is a dead body. And he manages to escape from prison at the end!

Can you work out his murderous route?

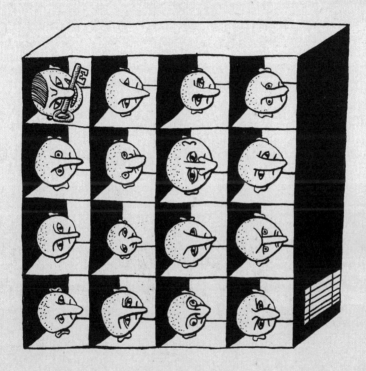

A CLOCK

Aucassin has one of the very first models of a verge-and-foliot clock. He never abandons it completely, but often forgets to wind it up.

Whenever it stops, he goes to the porch of the cathedral (whose façade includes a clock) to find Nicolette, the young Saracen women with whom he has fallen in love, then goes back home and resets his clock to the correct time.

How does he manage this, given that he does not know the length of his journey, but knows that he walks as fast on the way to the cathedral as he does on the return journey?

Solution on page 293

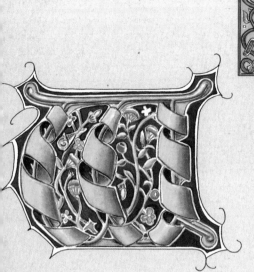

WHERE IS THE FATHER?

Lady Bertha is twenty-one years older than her son.
In six years, he will be one-fifth of his mother's age.

Question:
Where is the father?

Solution on page 294

 PHINX

What animal has four feet in the morning, two at noon, and three in the evening?

Solution on page 295

 HILDREN

Godfrey de Bouillon has five children. Half of them are daughters.
How can this be?

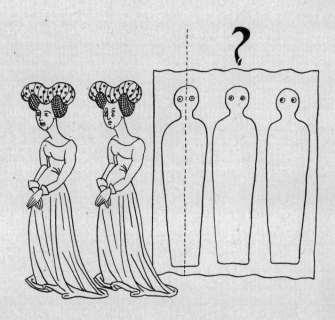

ARSENIC

The queen wants to get rid of the king's favourite.
Taking advantage of the fact that her rival is ill and
must take a medicinal pill each day, she calls on the
services of a poisoner, to whom she passes twelve boxes
of twelve pills, to be replaced by poison.

But the old witch dies before she can complete her
sinister task, and she has only had time to substitute
arsenic pills for the twelve pills contained in one box.

The queen knows that the arsenic pills weigh
1 oz less than the others, which weigh 10 oz.
How can she, with the help of a steelyard (a
balance with only one tray), find the box that
has been tampered with?

Solution on page 297

AGNETISM

You have two iron cylinders 6 inches long, with a base ½ inch in diameter. These two cylinders are identical in all respects, except that one is magnetized at both ends and the other is not. If you are in a locked room whose sole piece of furniture is a wooden table and without any other metallic object except for these two cylinders, how can you determine which of the two cylinders is magnetized?

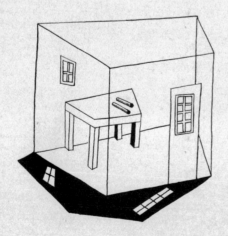

Solution on page 298

 RIDGE CROSSING

The bridgekeeper is a terrifying ghoul who appears every 17 minutes. Four people must cross this bridge. Each of them walks at a given maximum speed.

Let us call A the person who can cross the bridge in 1 minute, B the person who can cross in 2 minutes, C the one who needs 5 minutes, and D the laggard who requires 10 minutes.

These four people only have one torch between them, and it is impossible to cross the bridge without this torch.

The bridge can only bear the weight of two people. In which order should they make their crossing?

Solution on page 299

PASSWORD

A papal legate wants to attend a secret meeting being held by heretical Cathar knights. To be admitted, he must give a password to the guard at the door. He hides nearby and listens as other people show up.

A man arrives. The guard says to him, 'Five,' the man replies, 'Four,' and the guard allows him to pass. A second man turns up. The guard says to him, 'Six,' to which he replies, 'Three,' and is allowed through. A last man appears. The guard says to him, 'Four,' he responds, 'Four,' and enters. Now it's the papal legate's turn. The guard says to him, 'Seven.' What should he answer to gain entry?

Solution on page 300

 EHIND BARS

When the torches in the corridor are extinguished, what does the prisoner see on the bars of his cell door?

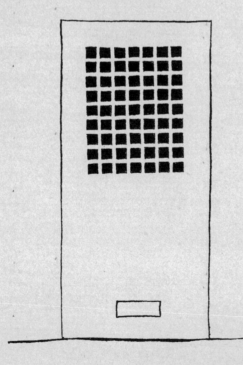

Solution on page 301

EAR

Approach and then draw back from the figure opposite, keeping your eyes fixed on the central point. What happens when you do this?

Solution on page 302

 ENS' EGGS

Eight hundred hens lay on average eight hundred eggs in eight days.

How many eggs do four hundred hens lay in four days?

Solution on page 303

ATS

If, in the kitchens of the castle, three cats catch three mice in 3 minutes, how many cats are needed to catch one hundred mice in 100 minutes?

Solution on page 304

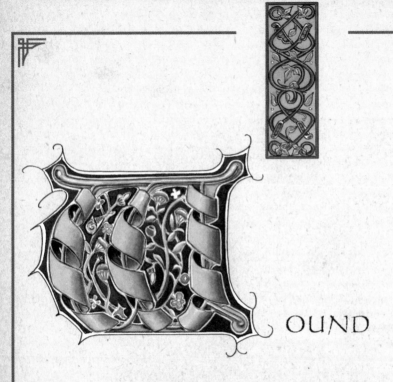

WOUND

During a chivalrous tournament, a man and his son are both competing. A lance impales the father, who dies on the spot.

His son, also wounded, is carried into a tent.

The doctor charged with examining him leans over the stretcher and exclaims, 'Good heavens! It's my son!'

How can this be?

Solution on page 305

ULE DRIVER

A mule tender is about to enter a lane with a sign reading, 'Mules Forbidden.'

He looks at the sign without grumbling and starts up the lane before being stopped by a soldier of the local constabulary.

The two converse for a moment and the mule driver continues unhindered.

How is this possible?

Solution on page 306

AIN COURTYARD

This figure represents the paving of a main courtyard.
How many squares does it have in all?

 OUNT THE TRIANGLES

Gazing at a multifaceted jewel resting on its base, the king's steward asks himself, 'How many triangles are there?'

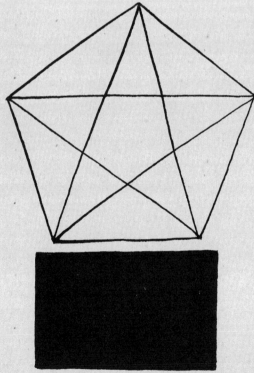

IVE ALIGNMENTS

Arrange these ten pieces to form five lines of four pieces each.

O YOUR QUILLS

Draw this figure without lifting your pencil from the paper or passing twice through the same spot.

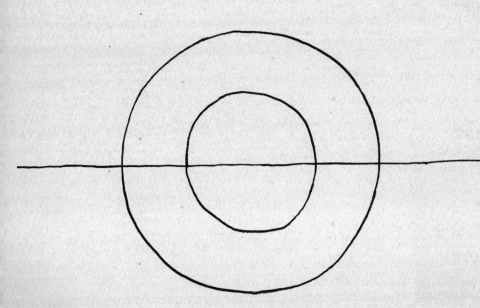

Solution on page 310

PART THREE

OWER TRANSFER

You need to transfer, one by one, all of the segments of the tower to the empty space on the right without ever placing a bigger segment on top of a smaller one, in a maximum of fifteen moves.

You can use the space in the middle as a transit point.

PAVED COURTYARD

In this courtyard, how would you describe the lines?

Solution on page 312

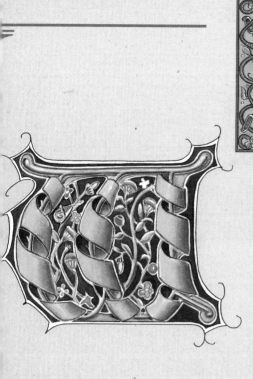

OOL STOCKINGS

Lady Brunehaut is untidy: all of her wool stockings (ten black stockings, eight red stockings, and six white stockings) are mixed together in a chest. She wants to take out a matched pair, but it's dark and the candles have gone out in her chamber.

What is the minimum number of stockings that Lady Brunehaut must remove from the chest to be certain of having two stockings of the same colour?

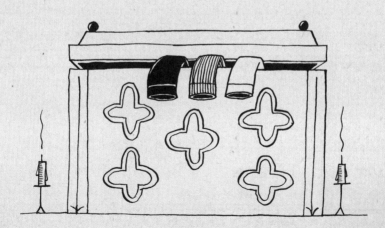

Solution on page 313

 HESTS

Some brigands are interrupted as they are robbing the king's treasury. They manage to carry off three chests, but they don't have the keys.

One of the chests contains gold coins, another silver, while the third has both gold and silver coins.

Each chest originally had a label indicating its contents, but during their flight, the brigands have mixed them up and all three labels are now attached to the wrong chests.

They can only spy one coin through the keyhole of each chest. Into which chest should they look in order to know right away what each chest contains?

Solution on page 314

ELEVEN BRANCHES

Two knights are contending for the hand of a lady at the royal court. To settle the matter, the king brings them before a table on which he has placed eleven branches.

Each of them in turn has the right to take away one, two, or three branches. The king decides that the knight who ends up taking the last branch shall renounce his claim.

Knowing that he will go first, how many branches should Gawain take in order to be sure of winning?

Solution on page 315

 HEEP

An old shepherd declares to his wife:

'When I die, I want our eldest son to receive half my sheep, our middle son to receive a third, and our youngest son a ninth. At the moment of his passing, the shepherd has seventeen sheep. After wracking their brains, his three sons fail to see any way to respect the will of their father, without carving up the sheep.

Eventually, another old shepherd, a friend of their father, finds the solution to their problem.

What does he propose?

Solution on page 316

ALUE OF THE PRODUCT

What is the value of the following product :
$(x - a) (x - b) (x - c) (x - d) (x - y) (x - z)$?

There are in all 26 parentheses, and a, b ... z can be any numbers (real or complex).

Solution on page 317

EAL NUMBERS ARE ALL POSITIVE?

We recall that R is the set of real numbers (positive or negative), informally described as those with an infinite decimal representation.
R = | - infinite, + infinity |

For all x in R $x^2 \$ 0$ [1] Well-known result.

For all x in R $(x^2)^{1/2} \$ 0^{1/2}$ [2] The two sides of the equation raised to the $1/2$ power.

For all x in R $x^{(2 \times 1/2)} = 0$ [3] Utilisation of the property: $(xn)m = xn \times m$

For all x in R $x^1 \$ 0$ [4] Simple calculation 2 x $1/2 = 1$

For all x in R $x \$ 0$ [5] Nicely done, isn't it?

Solution on page 318

# LTERNATION

Four black pieces and four white pieces are arranged as follows:

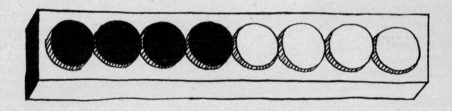

By carrying out a maximum of four moves, make them alternate: black-white-black, etc.

Hint: Each movement consists in shifting two adjacent pieces simultaneously.

Solution on page 319

PURSES

How can you alternate purses full of coins and empty purses by only touching a single purse?

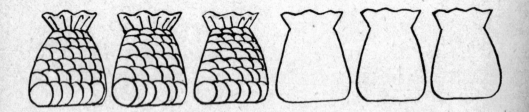

Solution on page 320

OW MUCH PROFIT?

At Provins fair, a merchant buys cloth for 70 shillings, and then sells it for 80 shillings.

Thinking he can earn more money, he buys it back for 90 shillings before finally selling it for 100 shillings.

Has he made a profit? If so, how many shillings has he earned?

Solution on page 321

AT THE MARKET

Lady Ermangarde is extravagant.

At the market, she has spent all she had in her purse at five different traders' shops. At each new shop, she spent 10 shillings more than half of what she had when she entered the establishment.

How much did she have in her purse when she started?

Solution on page 322

DECAPITATION

During a crusade, the king of France and his retinue are captured by the Saracens who have a cruel fate in store for their prisoners:
- the king is decapitated;
- his eldest son is hanged;
- two squires lose their head.

Yet this massacre results in only two victims.

How is this possible?

Solution on page 323

MPTY GLASS

How many drops of water can be put into an empty goblet?

Solution on page 324

 OUR CARDS AND FOUR LETTERS

Four cards are presented to you. They all bear a letter of the alphabet (either D, or G, or P, or L) on both sides.

How many times do you need to turn them over to verify the proposition:

'Behind every G, there is an L?'

Solution on page 325

CARD BRAIN-TEASER

A tumbler draws three cards at random from a deck of fifty-two and lays them out before him.

Can you determine which cards these are, and their order, with the help of the following four clues?

Clue 1:
A 5 is to the right of a king
(but not necessarily next to it).

Clue 2:
A club is to the left of a spade
(but not necessarily next to it).

Clue 3:
A 10 is to the left of a heart
(but not necessarily next to it).

Clue 4:
A heart is to the left of a spade
(but not necessarily next to it).

 USES

Merlin must let a potion settle for exactly 45 minutes, but he has no device for measuring time.

On the other hand, he does have a torch and two fuses, which he knows burn in 1 hour, but in an irregular fashion (half of a fuse will not be consumed in 30 minutes).

How can the wizard measure exactly 45 minutes?

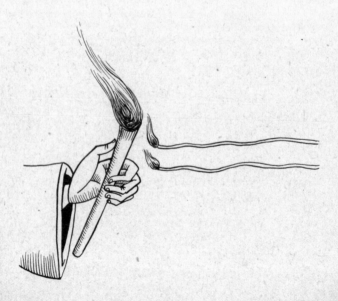

Solution on page 327

PADLOCK

As a token of her love, Isolde wishes to send Tristan a casket containing locks of her hair. So that no one else can open this incriminating box, Tristan and Isolde each possess a padlock that will secure the casket.

However, in order to avoid discovery, neither of the two lovers can have the padlock key belonging to the other.

How should the lovers proceed so when Tristan receives the sealed casket he is able to open it?

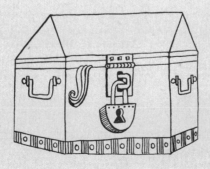

Solution on page 328

DRAGONFLY

Tristan and Isolde are separated by 100 furlongs.

They decide to meet, travelling in sedan chairs that are borne by porters at a speed of 10 furlongs per hour.

A dragonfly, whose speed is 150 furlongs per hour, then starts an uninterrupted journey back and forth between the two sedan chairs.

What distance has it travelled at the moment when the two lovers finally meet?

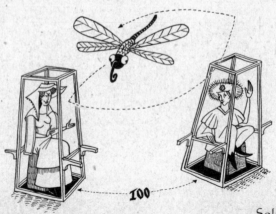

100

Solution on page 329

PALINDROME

A knight has ridden 15951 furlongs since he has been in the service of Pepin the Short. He notices that this number is a palindrome (it reads the same from left to right as it does from right to left).

He rides on, and two hours later the total number of furlongs he has travelled is once again a palindrome. How fast is he riding?

Solution on page 330

UINEVERE

To punish Guinevere for her infidelity, King Arthur locks her up in one of the impregnable round towers of his castle.

Full of sorrow, the queen, starting from the door, which is not facing due south, first walks towards the north of the tower over a distance of 30 paces before bumping into the wall. She then decides to go in a straight line west and runs into the wall again after 40 paces.

What is the diameter of the tower?

Solution on page 331

ATER LILY

A water lily doubling its surface area every year covers an entire pond at the end of ten years.

If there had been two water lilies with the same properties, how much time would it have taken to cover the pond entirely?

Solution on page 332

 IRD BECOMES DRAGON

Study this enclosure holding both birds and dragons.
Knowing that if you open locks 5, 6, 7 and 8, the animals in
the corresponding column will permutate (the birds becoming
dragons, and vice versa), and that the same will occur in the
corresponding rows if you open locks 1, 2, 3 and 4, how many
times do you need to open locks in order to change all the birds
in the enclosure into dragons?

Solution on page 333

 LIMBING SNAIL

A snail wants to climb to the top of a wall that is 10yds high.

But it moves in a very particular fashion: during the course of the day it climbs 3yds, and during the night, it descends 2yds.

If it starts its ascent one morning, how many days will it require to reach the top of this wall?

Hint:
10 days is not the correct answer.

Solution on page 334

EAR HUNT

A hunter seeks to kill a bear. He spots one and wants to take it by surprise. In order to go around it, the hunter travels on foot 5 miles to the south, then 5 miles east, and finally 5 miles north... And there, much to his dismay, he finds himself face-to-face with the bear, which has not moved at all.

Question:
What is the colour of the bear?

Solution on page 335

 IGITAL DISPLAY

On a clock with a digital display, how many times per day does the number 1 appear?

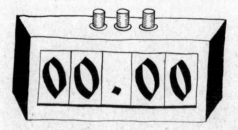

Solution on page 336

 URVEYOR

How can you divide this meadow into four parts with the same area and shape?

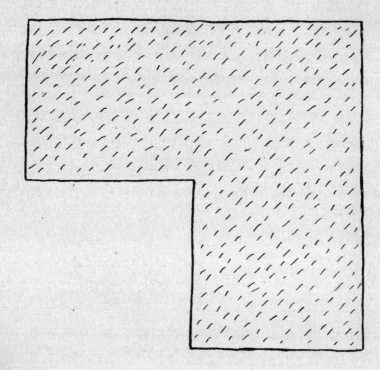

PRISON

Seven prisoners are locked up in a tower of the royal castle. To prevent them killing one another, the provost decides to separate them by erecting three walls. How should these walls be placed, if the size of each cell is of no importance?

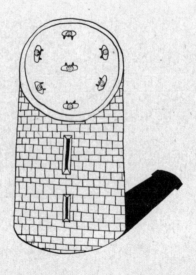

Solution on page 338

T THE INN

A rag trader, a draper and a tapestry-maker, all on their way to the Stourbridge fair, stop off at an inn in Cambridge where they rent a room for three persons costing 30 pennies for the night.

Each of them thus gives 10 pennies. Since the innkeeper takes a liking to them, he reduces the price to 25 pennies and returns 5 pennies. But as there are three of them, they decide to take 1 penny each and to leave 2 pennies as a tip. Each of them has paid 9 pennies (3 x 9 = 27) and the innkeeper has recovered 2 pennies.

$$27 + 2 = 29$$

Where did the thirtieth penny go?

Solution on page 339

DEAFNESS

The abbey's paschal candle has gone out and Friar Benedict is charged with re-lighting it as soon as he receives a signal from one of the three monks located in the crypt beneath the abbey's chapel.

But Friar Benedict is a bit deaf from ringing the abbey's bells, and only one of the three monks is capable of yelling loud enough for Benedict to hear him.

The abbot, who is also in the crypt, wants to know which monk can do this. What must he do to find out which monk Friar Benedict can hear, if he only goes upstairs to the chapel once?

Note: the abbot cannot be helped by anyone else and he cannot see into the chapel from the crypt.

Hints:
It is possible to check something else about the candle other than whether or not it is alight. The monks can ask Benedict to light it or to extinguish it.

Solution on page 340

WO GUARDS

A prisoner is locked up in a tower which has two doors. One of them leads to the exit, the other to the dungeon. A guard is placed before each door. One of them always tells the truth, the other always lies.

What single question can the prisoner ask of just one of these two guards to be sure of finding the door that leads to freedom?

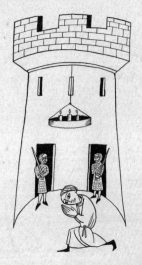

Solution on page 341

 UCKY DRAW

A tyrannical king has captured his most bitter opponent.
The next day, he gives the man a last chance to be pardoned.
He places two marbles in a helmet, one white symbolising
freedom, and one black representing death.

In front of the people gathered for the occasion, the prisoner must
draw unseen a single marble which will decide his fate.

The night before, a spy informs the prisoner that the king has
placed two black marbles in the helmet.

What should he do to ensure that he will be set free, after
drawing a single marble?

Solution on page 342

OME MENTAL CALCULATIONS

We can use four 1s in an equation to produce quite different totals:

1 1 1 1 = 3

1 1 1 1 = 4

using different arithmetical operations to arrive at the correct result:

$1 + 1 + (1 \times 1) = 3$

$(1 + 1) \times (1 + 1) = 4$

In each case, several possibilities exist.

In the table below, how, using each number in the first column exactly four times, and by inserting between them just three of the arithmetical signs + - × ÷, can you obtain each of the numbers in the second column?

×	Numbers
2	0, 1, 2, 3, 4, 5, 6, 10, 12
3	3, 4, 5, 6, 7, 8, 9, 10
4	3, 6, 7, 8, 24, 28, 32, 48
5	3, 5, 6, 26, 30, 50, 55, 120

Solution on page 343

ADDITION

How can you obtain 1,000 from a numerical addition containing only 8s?

Solution on page 344

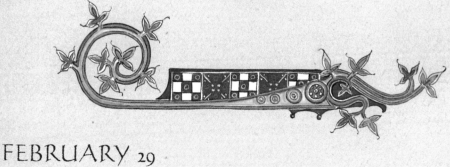

FEBRUARY 29

The son of Lady Gertrude and Sir Baldwin was born
on a Monday, February 29. How old will he be the next
time his birthday falls on a Monday?

Solution on page 345

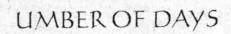UMBER OF DAYS

Certain months have thirty-one days and others only have thirty.

How many months had twenty-eight days between January 1008 and December 1012?

Solution on page 346

IVE TRIANGLES

An alchemist wants to move four matches to form five triangles. How should he do this?

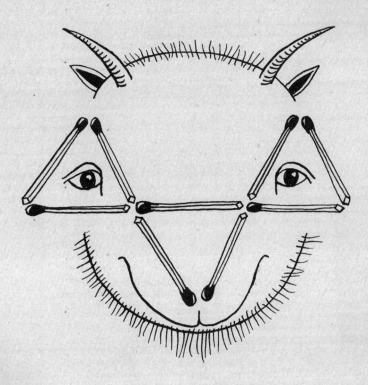

Solution on page 347

ATCHES 3

This time, the alchemist's apprentice wants to move four matches to obtain three equilateral trangles that touch one another. No open or incomplete triangles must remain.

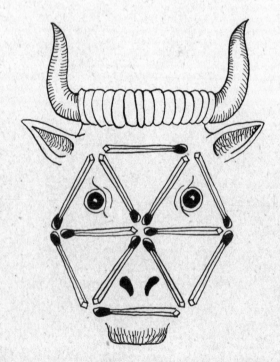

Solution on page 348

UNIVERSITY

At the University, a master poses a problem to the young clerics he teaches:

1. It's better than God.
2. It's worse than the Devil.
3. The poor have it.
4. The rich need it.
5. And if you eat it, you die.

What is it?

Solution on page 349

HADOW OF THE TOWER

In the shadow of the tower, strange phenomena occur...
What difference do you see between square A and square B?

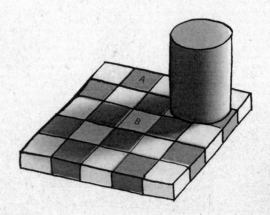

ABRIC CLIPPING

When do the diagonal lines on this swatch of fabric meet?

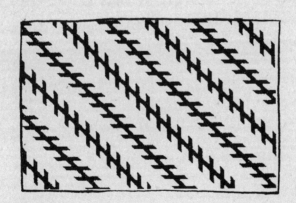

Solution on page 351

POWER OF COINS

Place fifteen coins in five stacks of three coins arranged in
a circle. After nine manoeuvres, you must end up with an
increasing number of coins in successive stacks (one coin in
stack A, two coins in stack B... five coins in stack E).

Each manoeuvre consists in distributing all of the coins
from any stack at the start, placing one coin in each of the
other stacks (even if empty) in clockwise order from the stack
you've selected. When all of the coins in that stack have been
distributed, you can then pick any other stack. What are the
nine manoeuvres involved?

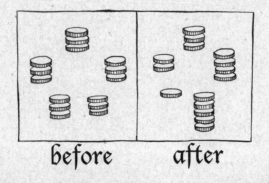

before   **after**

Solution on page 352

AGIC SQUARE

A tumbler, with a penny coin, a tuppence coin, and a threepenny bit arranged before him as shown above, issues a challenge to passers-by in front of Wells cathedral: 'The sum of the rows and columns in this magic square are equal to 6, but for it to be truly "magic," the diagonals should also be equal to 6. Who can tell me which three coins need to be moved in order to achieve this?'

Solution on page 353

 LICES OF CAKE

The king's cook has baked a cake with prunes.

How can he cut it up into eight identical pieces with just three knife strokes?

Solution on page 354

PANCAKES

The baker must bake three wheat pancakes, but can only place two at a time in his oven.

Knowing that it requires 3 minutes of baking per side, what is the minimum time needed to bake the three pancakes?

Solution on page 355

PART FOUR

WHAT DAY?

If today isn't the day after Monday or the day before Thursday, if tomorrow isn't Sunday, if it wasn't Sunday yesterday, and if the day before yesterday wasn't Wednesday, what day is it today?

Solution on page 356

STRANGE DATE

In what respect was November 29, 1192, the year marking the end of the Third Crusade, a peculiar day?

Solution on page 357

ITTLE RECTANGLE BECOMES SQUARE

Here is a rectangular parchment whose length (L = 2) is twice its width (w = 1)

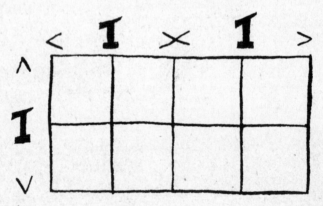

(In the diagram, the scale is 1 : 2)

How can you cut up this parchment in order to make a square with the same surface area, using the pieces?

Solution on page 358

 **ONG RECTANGLE BECOMES SQUARE**

Here is a rectangular parchment whose length (L) measures 5 and width (w) measures 1.

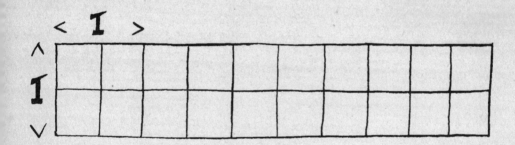

(In the diagram, the scale is 1 : 2)

How can you cut up this parchment in order to make a square with the same surface area, using the pieces?

Solution on page 359

A LLEGIANCE

Robin Hood captures two knights, Sir Thomas and Sir Robert, in Sherwood Forest.

One of them has pledged allegiance to Prince John, the other to King Richard.

When the thief asks them to whom they owe allegiance, Sir Thomas declares, 'I am the bondsman of Prince John,' while Sir Robert says, 'I am the bondsman of King Richard.'

Friar Tuck, who knows both men, affirms that at least one of the pair is lying.

How can Robin Hood determine the truth?

Solution on page 360

 ERFS

A great lord is invited to stay with his cousin, the duke of Burgundy. Wishing to impress their guest, Lady Margaret, the duchess, asserts: 'More than a hundred serfs work on the lands belonging to my husband.'

Young Eudes, the duke's son, disputes this: 'Not at all! I'm certain there are less than a hundred.' Blanche, the duke's daughter, adds, 'Well, I'm sure there is at least one.'

If only one of these assertions is true, how many serfs work the land owned by the duke of Burgundy?

Solution on page 361

 ASUALTIES OF WAR

If 70% of soldiers have lost their eye during the course of a battle, 75% an ear, 80% an arm, and 85% a leg, what is the minimum percentage that have lost an eye, an ear, an arm, and a leg, all in this same battle?

Solution on page 362

RABBIT FEET

Landry raises chickens and rabbits.
When he counts heads, he finds eight.
When he counts feet, he finds twenty-eight.
How many rabbits does he have? And how many chickens?

Solution on page 363

ROHIBITION

Read this sign once and then turn quickly to the solution.

!

Please
leave your
weapons at
at the castle gates

Solution on page 364

FFF

After counting them just once, can you say how many Fs are there
are in this text?

finished files are the
result of years of
scientific study
combined with the
experience of years

Solution on page 365

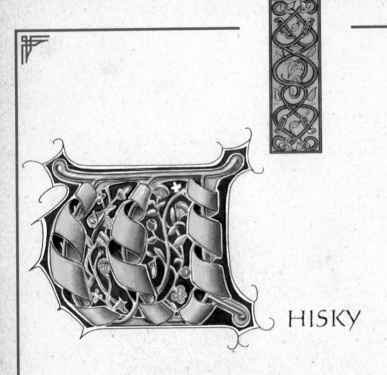

WHISKY

What is unusual about this sentence?

'Did you know that Irish whiskey, often judged superior to the Scottish variety, existed from the beginning of the Middle Ages and quite often won prizes at medieval fairs?'

26 years old

Solution on page 366

OGICAL SERIES 4

Complete this series:

1 3 5 4 4 4...

RAB NUMERAL EQUATION

The following equation is not true:
What must be done, by adding a single stroke, to make this equation correct, other than crossing the = sign and converting it to ≠ ?

$$5+5+5=550$$

Solution on page 368

ATCHTOWER

Here is a watchtower on which eight sentinels are standing. How can this tower be divided into four identical zones, each guarded by two sentinels?

Solution on page 369

TRAIGHT LINES

Can the copyist link these sixteen points by drawing six straight lines without lifting his quill from the paper?

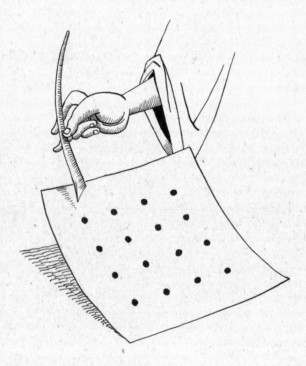

Solution on page 370

HE WORM IN THE MANUSCRIPT

A ten-volume manuscript is stored in the correct order on a library shelf.

Each volume is 4½ inches thick, with two covers, each ½ inch thick. A worm, starting on page 1 of volume I, eats its way in a straight line through the complete set and finishes on the last page of the last volume.

What distance does it travel in the course of its journey?

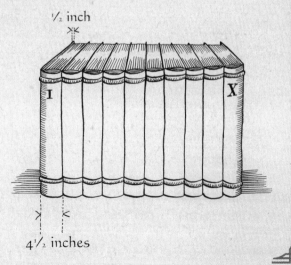

½ inch

I

X

4½ inches

Solution on page 371

EETING

Some monks leave Cluny abbey headed for the abbey at Clairvaux. An hour later, another group of monks leaves Clairvaux in the direction of Cluny.

Knowing that the first group walks 5 miles in an hour, while the second group advances at the slower pace of 3 miles per hour, which group of monks is closer to Cluny abbey when the two parties meet?

Solution on page 372

LOGICAL SERIES 5

The king wants to test his ministers and asks them to complete this series:

1
11
21
1211
111221
312211

Solution on page 373

O 4 IN THE SERIES

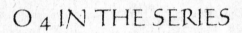

For those who solved the preceding puzzle (or read the solution!), here is another question concerning the same series: show why the figure 4 can never appear.

Solution on page 374

 ISHING

Two fathers accompanied by their respective sons go fishing.
Each person catches a fish. Yet only three fish are caught. Why?

Solution on page 376

 ART

A cart-driver is rolling along in his cart at a brisk speed, in the country, without a lantern to light his way. There is no moonlight. A woman dressed in black passes in front of him. Despite these conditions, he manages to see her and stops before running into her. Why?

Solution on page 377

N THE PURSE

A monkey has stolen a purse containing two coins, which together are worth 30 groats.

Given that one of the coins is not a 10-groat piece, and that the only coins that exist are 1, 5, 10, and 20 groats, can you say how much each of the two coins is worth?

Solution on page 378

HAIN

Sir Godfrey wants to forge a closed chain with the help of these four pieces, in order to offer it as a gift to Lady Margot:

Breaking a link costs five sovereigns and one needs to pay ten to have it reforged. What is cheapest way to make a closed chain, and how much will this cost Sir Godfrey?

Solution on page 379

HREE-WAY GAME

Three fellows, Martin, Eberulf and Leander, are finishing a game that is played in five rounds. They have been betting with 1-shilling pieces and throughout the game have only played with amounts in whole numbers.

In each round, the loser has doubled the holdings of the two other players. At the end of the game, Martin has 8 shillings, Eberulf has 9, and Leander has 10.

How much did each player have at the start of the game?

Solution on page 380

 NKWELL

An inkwell and quill costs 11 shillings. The inkwell is worth 10 shillings more than the quill. How much is the inkwell, and how much is the quill?

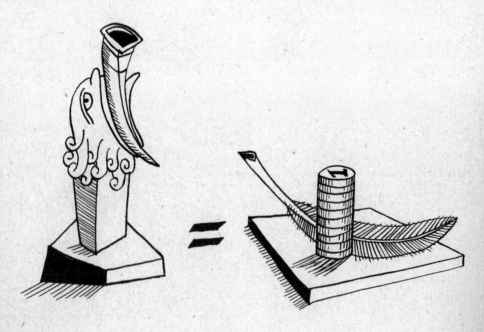

 EAPFROG

What is the minimum number of moves required by the demon to reverse the order of the pieces (so that the black ones are on the right and the white ones are on the left), given that:
  - a piece can advance one space only,
  - one piece can leap over another if it lands on an empty space.

Solution on page 383

ATHEDRAL

An architect draws a plan for a Gothic cathedral including twelve pillars arranged in a Latin cross. If one counts the pillars from A to B, from A to C, or from A to D, one finds a total of eight pillars. But lacking the money needed to carry out this project, the architect must draft a new plan, with the Latin cross for his cathedral using only ten pillars, but without changing the number of pillars on the axes AB, AC, and AD, that is, eight pillars.

How does he place the pillars to achieve this?

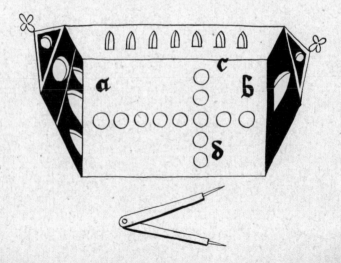

Solution on page 384

UELS

A chivalrous tournament with n participants is organized. The principle is direct elimination: a knight who has lost a duel against an adversary must leave the competition.

How does the number of duels (including the final) vary as a function of the number of knights taking part in the tournament?

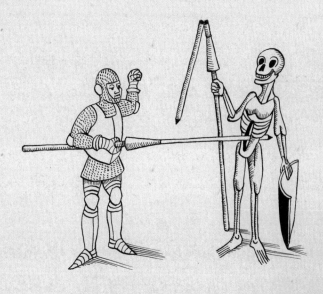

Solution on page 385

WO BROTHERS

Peter and Johannes are two brothers. They want to determine which of them is the better horseman, but their father only possesses one horse.

To test themselves, they decide to make a circuit of the town's outer defensive wall, which comprises twenty-four towers placed equidistantly from one another.

Peter rides the horse to begin with, from the first to the twelfth tower, while Johannes, sitting behind him, times him with the help of an hourglass.

Next from the twelfth to the twenty-fourth tower, it is Johannes who holds the reins, with Peter behind him as timekeeper.

Peter wins easily. Could this result have been predicted from the start?

Solution on page 386

HREE DAUGHTERS

To a peasant woman who asks the age of her three daughters, a woman replies:

'Multiply their ages, and the product is thirty-six.'

'I can't work out their ages from that.'

'The sum of their three ages is equal to the number of eggs that I have my basket.'

The peasant woman counts the eggs but continues to grumble:

'I still don't see.'

'The eldest is blonde.'

'Oh yes, now I know!'

How did she find the answer? What ages are the three girls?

Solution on page 388

 OSEBUSH

Sister Blanche plants a rosebush in the gardens of Fontevrault abbey. To another nun who enquires about the size of the rosebush, she replies:

'It measures 30 inches, plus half its own height.'

How tall is the rosebush?

Solution on page 390

ANDLES

Friar Luke is the steward of the abbey. Very economical, he recycles the stubs of used candles to make new ones. He is capable of reconstituting a candle from three candle stubs which he melts together. How many candles can he make from the nine candle stubs that he has recovered this morning from the abbey's chapel?

Solution on page 391

IRE

The troops of Louis IX enter, from the west, into an immense forest 30 miles long, and begin to move eastwards. Their maximum marching speed in the dense forest is 8 miles per hour. On this day the wind is blowing at 50 miles per hour towards the east.

An hour later, the enemy troops light a fire at the western border of the forest, across its entire width.

The wind then propagates the fire eastwards at 50 miles per hour. The king realizes that the fire will overtake his troops before they can leave the forest.

How does he save his men?

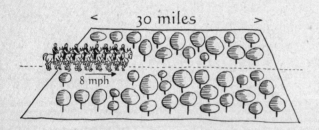

< 30 miles >

8 mph

50 mph

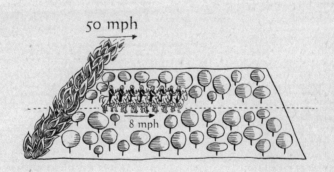

8 mph

Solution on page 392

REVERSIBLE TRIANGLE

An archer lets fly a series of arrows forming a triangle whose point is on the left. How can you obtain a similar triangle, but with the point on the right, by moving just three arrows?

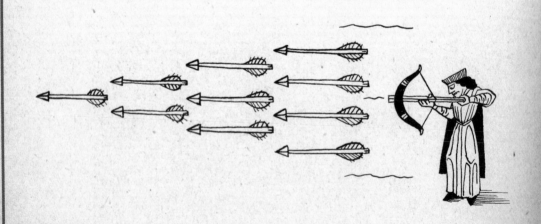

Solution on page 394

ROSE WINDOW

Looking at the rose window of the cathedral, Friar Francis wonders, 'Which grey circle is bigger, the one above or the one below?'

Solution on page 395

 OGICAL SERIES 6

Upon the cover of a dusty manuscript in the great library Friar Claude discovers these symbols. Help him complete this series.

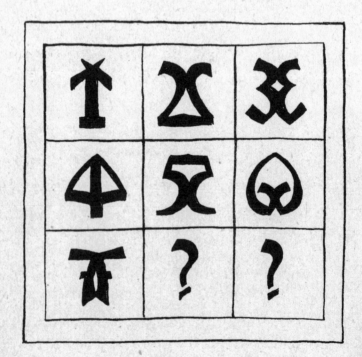

 ATHER AND SON

If you add the year of birth of a father, that of his son, the age of the father, and the age of the son, what result to do you obtain?

Solution on page 397

TORTURE

You are about to be interrogated under torture. The torturer does you a favour: 'You can make a final declaration that will determine the manner in which you will die. If your affirmation is false, you will be drawn and quartered, but if it's true, you will be burnt alive!'

Not finding either of these alternatives appealing, you seek to make a declaration that will get you out of this dire situation. What should you say?

Solution on page 398

ANCE

A knight, armed with a lance five feet long, presents himself before the portcullis of the castle belonging to his feudal lord. The guard on duty denies him entry to the castle, on the grounds that objects over four feet long are forbidden within.

The knight then goes off to see a carpenter, who makes him a case in which to place his lance. The knight then returns to the castle with the case, and this time, the guard lets him enter.

How is that possible?

Solution on page 399

 TAIRCASE

A Florentine architect can build the spiral staircase for a castle in six weeks.

A Flemish architect can complete the same staircase in just three weeks.

How long would it take them to build the castle staircase if they joined forces?

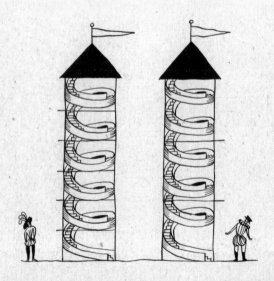

Solution on page 400

A MILLION HAIRS

Before the Black Death ravaged Europe in the 14th century, the kingdom of France had about sixteen million inhabitants, and none of them possessed more than a million hairs on their head.

Can one be certain that there were at least two inhabitants in the kingdom who had exactly the same number of hairs on their head?

Solution on page 401

HREE SWISS

Three Swiss share a brother. When this brother dies, the three Swiss no longer have a brother.

How is this possible, knowing that it is not a question of a half-brother?

Solution on page 402

DUE SOUTH HOUSE

The four façades of the house all face due South.
How is this possible?

Solution on page 403

 ASTIME

The duke of Clarence's cook is preparing a pheasant that his master has brought back from the hunt. He wants to accompany it with a wine sauce that needs to be reduced over exctly 9 minutes.

He has two hourglasses, a big one allowing him to time 7 minutes, and a little one allowing him to measure 4 minutes.

What should he do to time the 9 minutes?

Solution on page 404

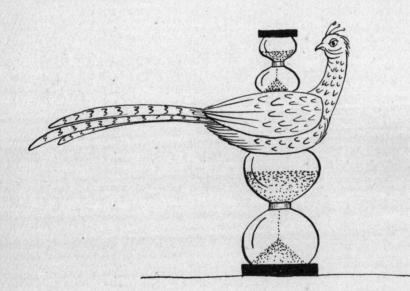

SOLUTIONS

 OVE POTION

At the end of step 6, there remains 4 fl oz in the 5 fl oz jar.

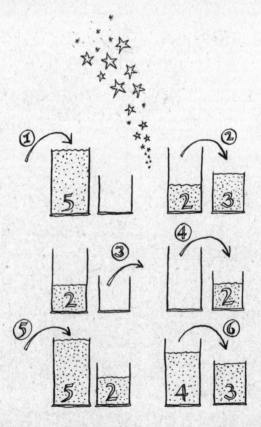

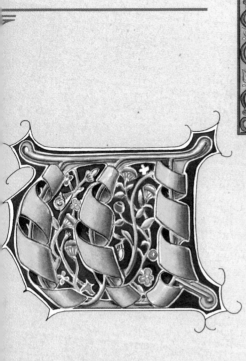

ATER IN THE WINE

Suppose that there was 80% water and 20% wine in the first mug at the end of the manoeuvre. The 20% of water that is missing must be in the other mug, as is the 80% of missing wine. To start with, there was the same amount of each liquid. The proportions in the second mug must thus be 20% water and 80% wine. The proportions are perfectly inverted: 80/20 as opposed to 20/80.

  So there is as much wine in the first mug as there is water in the second, and as much wine in the second as there is water in the first.

 YCLING RACE

Roland finishes fourth. By passing the rider in second place, he puts himself in second (and not in first). So when the two other competitors pass him, he falls back into fourth position.

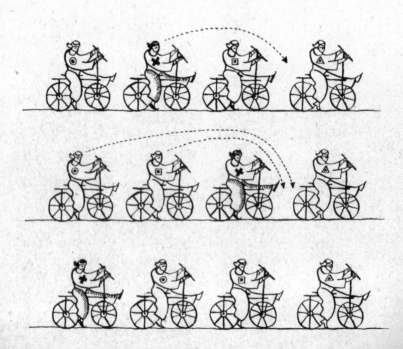

 ELLS

The three seconds that go by in ringing four o'clock correspond to the intervals between bell tolls, not the number of tolls. To ring the twelve tolls of midday, Quasimodo will take eleven seconds, corresponding to the eleven intervals separating the twelve tolls of the bell.

RIANGLE TRICK

Here's one solution:

RAIN-TEASER

a	b	c	d	e
c	d	e	a	b
e	a	b	c	d
b	c	d	e	a
d	e	a	b	c

INSHIP BOND

The father of my son = me (logical, isn't it?).
So the sentence becomes: 'If the son of this man, is "me", what is the kinship bond between this man and me?'

Which is quite simple: this man is your father.

Solution for page 28

 UM OF 1 TO 100

We know that:

1 + 100 = 101

2 + 99 = 101

etc.

So the sum equals:

50 × 101 = 5,050

Seen in another way:

$1 + 2 + 3 + ... + (n - 1) + n = n(n + 1) ÷ 2$

with n = 100

$1 + 2 + 3 + ... + 100 = 100 × 101 ÷ 2 = 5,050$

Solution for page 29

A PLACE OF THEIR OWN

All you need to do is place them back to back!

ᴍENTAL CALCULATION

Unless you've made a mistake, you
should have 80.

Because $30 \div (1 \div 2) = 30 \times 2 = 60$

$60 + 20 = 80$

 UT-UP SQUARE

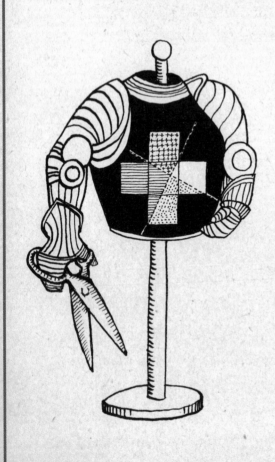

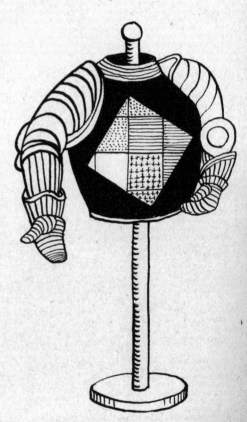

 ISH

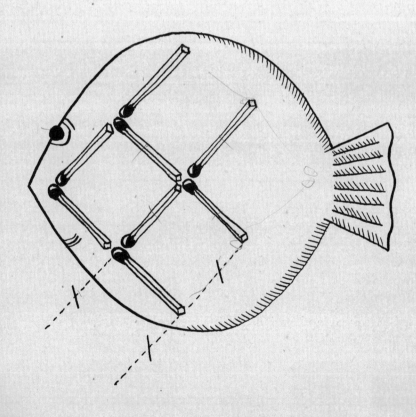

ATCH TRIANGLES 1

All the carpenter's apprentice needs to do is to construct a Star of David (who said the triangles had to be all the same size?)

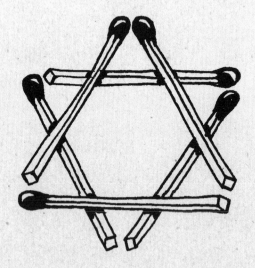

We often look for difficult answers to easy questions.

Solution for page 35

HE MONK AND THE MOUNTAIN

The answer is yes. To make it obvious, suppose we have two monks who both depart at 9am: one starts from the bottom of the mountain and the other from the top. Since they are both on the same path, they will have to meet each other!

Solution for page 36

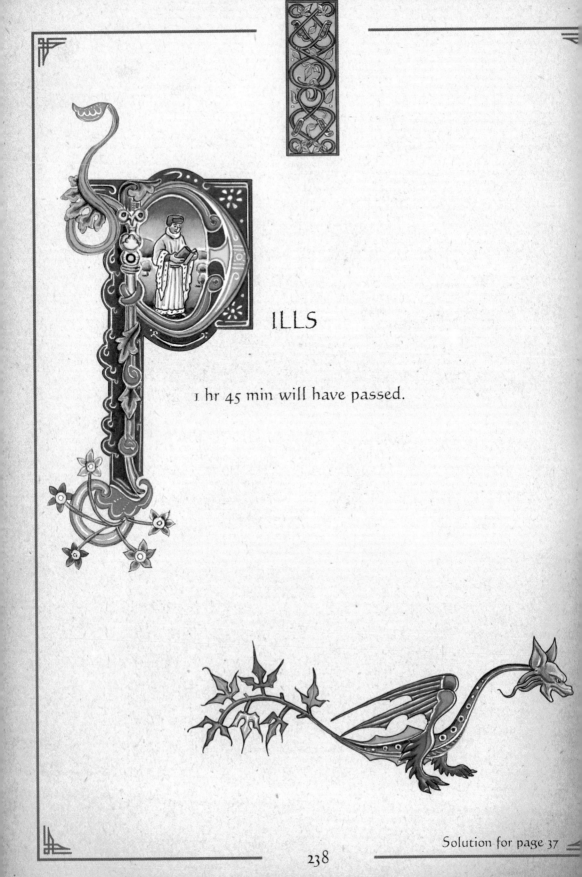

ILLS

1 hr 45 min will have passed.

SHIELD TRIANGLES

The two shields are not actually triangles. Look closely at points A, D, and G: they are not aligned.

In fact, the slope of the hypotenuse of triangle ADB is different from that of triangle DGE: point D would be slightly to the right of the straight line AG if we took the trouble to draw it. And similarly in the case of point F. From this fact it follows that figure ACFGD has a surface area that is less than an imaginary triangle ACG. In the same way, on the second shield, points HJL and IKL are not aligned: points J and K are outside of a triangle HIL. From the fact that the first shield has a surface area that is less than a 'true' triangle, it's that there is a difference in area between the two. In the last diagram, the two shields are superimposed. If they formed triangles, the surface AJGD would have an area of zero.

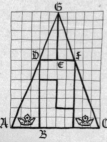
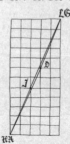

Solution for page 38

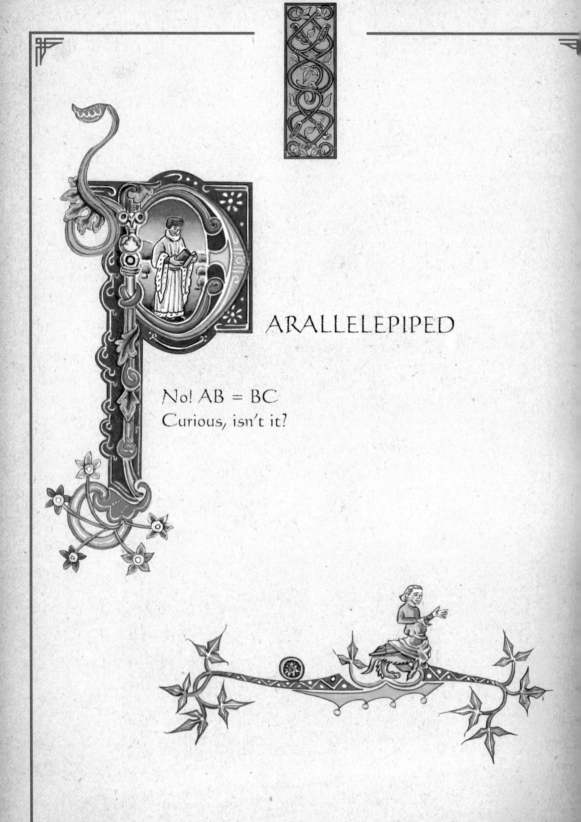

ARALLELEPIPED

No! AB = BC
Curious, isn't it?

Solution for page 40

$$1 = 2\ ?$$

The error is located between line 6 and line 7.

We divided by (a - b)... which is equal to 0. Division by 0 is, of course, impossible.

BRACADABRA

You don't have any choice where the initial A is concerned.

Then you have two possibilities for the B, and following that, two possibilities between your chosen B and the next two R's. And so on, down the ten rows where you have a choice.

This gives you 2^{10} ways of reading the word ABRACADABRA, that is, 1,024.

WO RESULTS FOR THE SAME NUMBER?

The answer to the question is yes!

It is true that $1 = 0.9999999999999\ldots$

And this calculation is proof of that.

Note: between lines 3 and 4, you need to remind yourself that infinity - 1 is still infinity.

Another (but less elegant) demonstration:

$$1 = 3 \times (1 \div 3) = 3 \times 0.3333333\ldots = 0.9999999\ldots$$

ECHANICAL ALARM CLOCK

You will sleep for an hour.

A clock with hands does not differentiate between 10am and 10pm. So it will go off at 10pm.

Solution for page 45

ROUBADOUR

He juggles!

If he was juggling with the objects all the way across the bridge, there was always an object that was not actually in the troubadour's hands.

LOGICAL SERIES 1

The terms of this series correspond to the initials of the numbers:
'One, Two, Three, Four, Five, Six, Seven, Eight, Nine, Ten...'

o t t f f s s 8 9 10
1 2 3 4 5 6 7 e n t

Solution for page 47

 LAZIERS

Here is one possible solution:

 HIELD OF NAILS

Solution for page 50

UESTION OF AGE

State of affairs:

Age	Before	Now
Master	x	40
Pupil	y	z

What do we know?

• $40 = 4 \times y$ because 'I am four times as old as you were'

so $y = 10$

Age	Before	Now
Master	x	40
Pupil	10	z

• $z = x$ because 'I was the same age as you are now'

Age	Before	Now
Master	x	40
Pupil	10	z (or x)

• The difference in their ages is the same at any given time, so:

$x - 40 = 10 - x$

$2 \times x = 50$

$x = 25$ The pupil is therefore 25 years old.

Solution for page 51

 HE GUARDS' HALL

In the Guards' Hall, there are as many weapons as there are men, that is, 600.

5% (or 30 of these men) carry one weapon. Among the 570 who remain, representing 95%, half of them carry two and the other half carry none: that is the same number of weapons as if they all carried one.

Which gives 570 + 30 = 600 weapons.

Solution for page 52

ATCH TRIANGLES 2

You need to think in 3D!

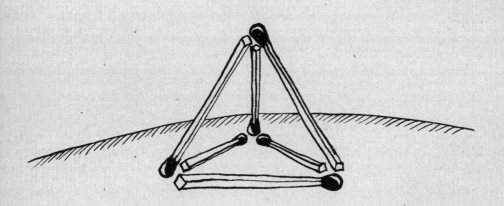

 ORK

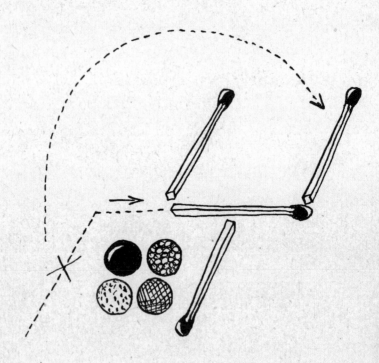

Solution for page 55

 YMBOLS

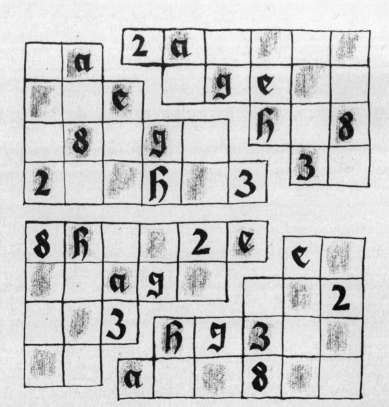

INE POINTS

Here's one way of doing this:

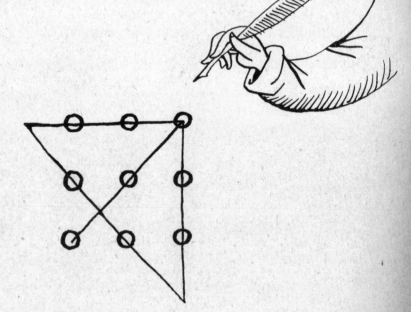

Nobody said you couldn't go outside the framework formed by the eight points...

Solution for page 57

INGLE FILE

a black feather on my helmet

Percival is the winner, affirming that there is a black feather on his helmet. His reasoning is as follows:

'I know that there are two black feathers and two white ones. Gawain can see me, so if my feather is the same colour as Galahad's, which he can also see, he would have deduced the colour of his own feather, which necessarily would have been different from ours. Since he remained silent, that means my feather is a different colour from Galahad's. I see that Galahad is wearing a white feather, so mine is black.'

Solution for page 58

 WOLF, A GOAT AND
A CABBAGE

You must first cross with the goat and leave it on its own while you cross back.

Then you must bring over the wolf and come back with the goat.

You leave the goat and cross over with the cabbage. Lastly, you return alone to the bank you started from and transfer the goat.

Solution for page 60

 UBTRACTION

Just once.

　After that, you're subtracting from 30, no longer from 36!

ANUSCRIPT

The pages of the manuscript bearing the number 9 are:
9-19-29-39-49-59-69-79-89-99 (be careful: there are two 9s in 99), but also:
90-91-92-93-94-95-96-97-98 which are often forgotten!
The cleric thus inscribes the number 9 20 times while numbering the pages of the manuscript.

ANDICAPS

You still have three senses remaining. For those who answered two, remember that speech is not a sense!

Solution for page 63

 ALL

All he needs to do is to urinate in the hole for the wicker ball to rise up to the surface!

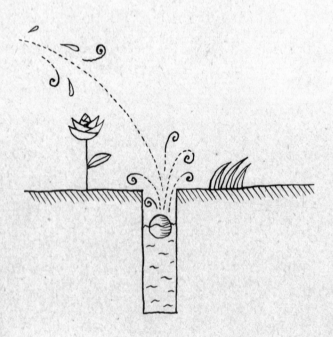

STANDARD

The numbers 1 and 8 have a characteristic distinct from the rest: they are the only numbers to have just one neighbour (respectively 2 and 7).

Following on from this, these two numbers are placed in the spaces at the centre of the standard (the ones with the greatest number of neighbours); then 2 and 7 are placed in the only spaces they can go in: these are the outermost spaces, 2 next to 8 and 7 next to 1. Lastly, the four remaining numbers are judiciously placed in the upper and lower spaces of the standard. One possible solution would be this:

And there you have it!

```
    6 4
  2 8 1 7
    5 3
```

RIANGLE AND SUMS

On the 1-2 side, we are missing 14 which we can get from either 5 + 9 or 6 + 8.

On the 2-3 side, we are missing 12 which we can get from either 4 + 8 or 5 + 7.

On the 1-3 side, we are missing 13 which we can get from either 4 + 9, or 5 + 8, or 6 + 7.

By elimination, that gives:

side 1-2: 5 + 9
side 2-3: 4 + 8
side 1-3: 6 + 7

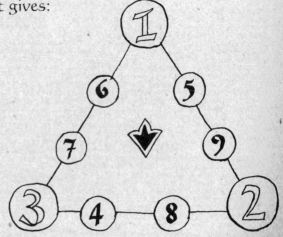

Solution for page 66

PRECIOUS STONES

1a. The king chooses at random three stones for the left-hand tray, and three for the right-hand one. If the trays are balanced, the fake is one of the other three stones (let us call them the 'heavier three') and he proceeds to step 2a.

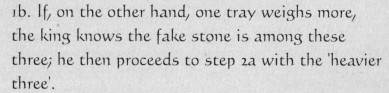

1b. If, on the other hand, one tray weighs more, the king knows the fake stone is among these three; he then proceeds to step 2a with the 'heavier three'.

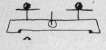

2a. The king chooses a stone at random from the 'heavier three' for the left-hand tray and another stone for the right-hand one. If the trays are balanced, he can deduce from this that the fake stone is the third in the trio.

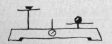

2b. If, however, one tray weighs more, that means the fake stone is sitting upon it.

Solution for page 67

 INE LEVEL

The men must lean the cask over until the wine comes right up to the brim, and then examine the bottom of the cask.

If they cannot see the bottom because it is covered by wine, then the cask is more than half-full.

If they can see any part of the bottom of the cask, then it is less than half-full.

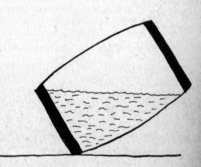

STRANGE EQUIVALENCE

In any period: 31 in octal (that is, in base 8) is always equal to 25 in the decimal system (that is, in base 10).

Base 10	Base 8		Base 10	Base 8
1 → 1			14 → 16	
2 → 2			15 → 17	
3 → 3			16 → 20	
4 → 4			17 → 21	
5 → 5			18 → 22	
6 → 6			19 → 23	
7 → 7			20 → 24	
8 → 10			21 → 25	
9 → 11			22 → 26	
10 → 12			23 → 27	
11 → 13			24 → 30	
12 → 14			25 → 31	
13 → 15			...	

Solution for page 69

 UT-UP

Solution for page 70

ATCHES 1

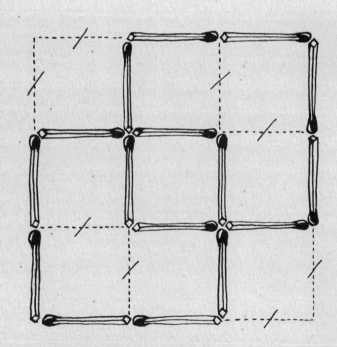

ONNECTIONS

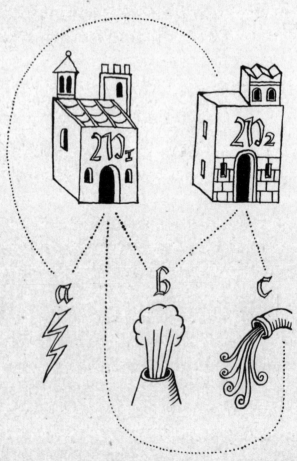

Solution for page 73

ATCHES 2

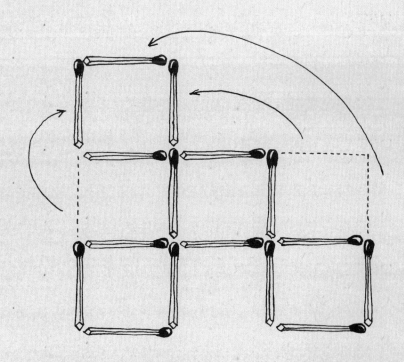

 LL IN THE HEAD

You obtain 1.

AKE 24 WITH 5, 5, 5, AND 1

$1 \div 5 = 0.2$

$5 - 0.2 = 4.8$

$4.8 \times 5 = 24$

Who said the numbers had to remain whole?

   Once again, we observe the natural tendency of the human mind to add unnecessary constraints when tackling problems…

Solution for page 78

PREDICTION

02/02/2000 marks the first time since 28/08/888 when all the numbers of the date were even.

Solution for page 79

TOURNAMENT

Only one person is heading for the tournament:

You!

Solution for page 80

E WHO LOSES WINS

Each knight has mounted the horse belonging to the other!

Solution for page 81

 Case n° 1

 Case n° 5

 Case n° 2

 Case n° 6

 Case n° 3

 Case n° 7

EADDRESS Case n° 4

The lady reasons as follows:

Case no. 1: impossible because the first lady would have answered 'YES' upon seeing two white headdresses, since her own could only be black.

Case no. 2: impossible because the second lady would have answered 'YES' upon seeing two white headdresses, since her own could only be black.

Case no.3: impossible because the second lady would have answered 'YES', taking into account the response of the first lady (case no. 1), since her own headdress could only be black.

Case no. 4: possible case.

Case no. 5: possible case.

Case no. 6: possible case.

Case no. 7: possible case.

Conclusion: in the last four possible cases, the blind lady's headdress can only be black, allowing her to answer 'YES.'

R

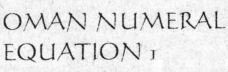

OMAN NUMERAL EQUATION 1

It has to be read backwards:

ROMAN NUMERAL EQUATION 2

(The square root of 1 equals 1.)

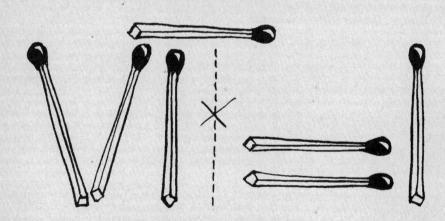

HOUGHT DETECTOR (1)

The symbol found is 'S.'

The result is always a multiple of 9 that is less than 90.
All one needs is a table showing the same symbol for 9, 18,
27, 36, 45, 54, 63, 72, and 81!

Solution for page 86

HOUGHT DETECTOR (2)

Sorry, there are no elephants in Denmark!

ATCH SQUARE

You need to take square in its arithmetic sense rather than the geometric one.

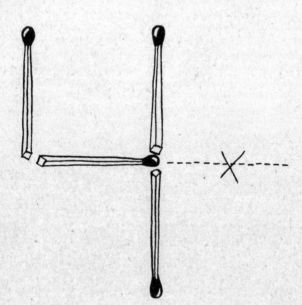

4 is the square of 2.

Solution for page 89

 IVE SQUARES

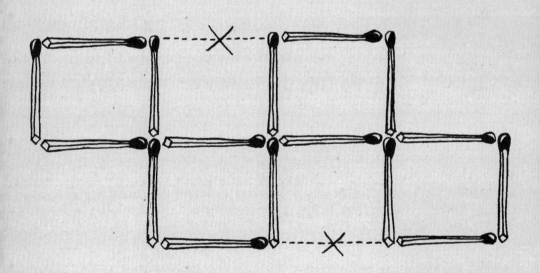

ATHS

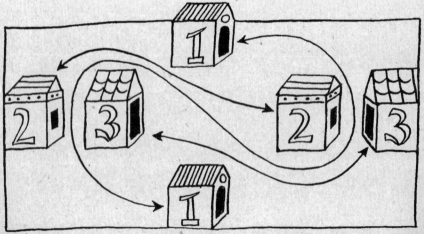

Solution for page 91

SOLATION

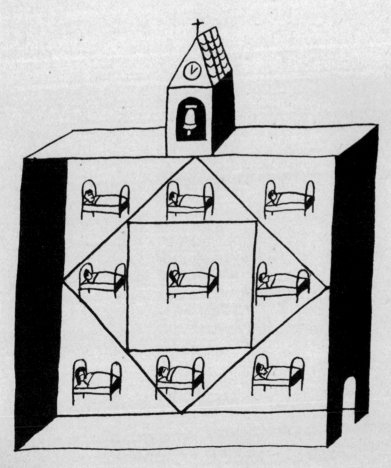

 IGHT QUEENS

Here's one solution::

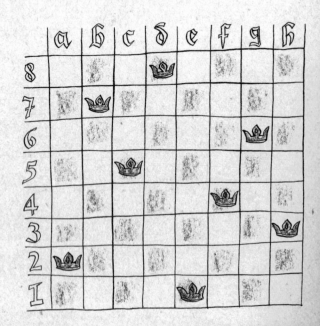

OUR QUEENS AND A BISHOP

One possible solution is to place the queens on C5, D3, E4, and H8, and lastly the bishop on A2.

 ICIOUS CIRCLE

Three won't do, because it contains an R.
   So the answer is four.
   The correct sentence is:
   'In this circle the "r" is present four times.'

Solution for page 95

CCURRENCES

To be true, the sentence must be completed in the following fashion:

'In this sentence, the number of occurrences of 0 is 1, of 1 is 7, of 2 is 3, of 3 is 2, of 4 is 1, of 5 is 1, of 6 is 1, of 7 is 2, of 8 is 1, and 9 is 1.'

The code for the strongbox is therefore: 1732111211
   To start with the only certainty is that the number of 0s is 1. You must then solve this brain-teaser by trial-and-error, the quickest route being to examine the 9 next, then the 8...

Solution for page 96

 ARPET

Here is the cut that needs to be made in the carpet:

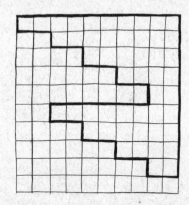

And this is how the entire chamber is covered:

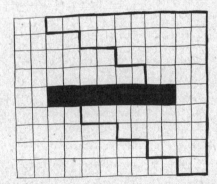

AVALON

Here's how to do it:

OGICAL SERIES 2

The terms of this series correspond to the last letters of the numbers onE twO threE fouR fivE siX seveN eighT…

…N T…

LOGICAL SERIES 3

1 (2,3) 2 (5,6) 4 (11,30) 26 (41,330) 304

The number in front of a parenthesis is the difference between the second number of the preceding parenthesis and the number in front of that parenthesis.

Example: $2 = 3 - 1$

The first number of each parenthesis is equal to the sum of the two numbers in the preceding parenthesis.

Example: $11 = 5 + 6$

The second number of each parenthesis is equal to the product of the two numbers in the preceding parenthesis

Example: $30 = 5 \times 6$

The three numbers that complete the series are therefore (41,330) 304:

$11 + 30 = 41$

$11 \times 30 = 330$

$330 - 26 = 304$

Solution for page 101

URDEROUS ITINERARY

The trick lies in returning to the first cell (which doesn't contain a dead body!) after the first murder...

There are several routes to a successful escape!

One possible solution is:

Solution for page 102

 LOCK

When Aucassin leaves home, he winds up his clock and sets it to 12 o'clock. When he goes to see Nicolette, he looks at the clock on the façade of the church to note his time of arrival and his time of departure. When he returns home, he looks at his verge-and-foliot clock and then knows how much time he has spent away from home.

By subtracting the time he spent with his girlfriend, he knows how much time he spent walking...

By adding half of this time to the time he left Nicolette, he is able to tel what time it really is.

HERE IS THE FATHER?

Let x be the age in years of the son and let y be the age in years of his mother, Lady Bertha.

Lady Bertha is twenty-one years older than her son. So we can assume that: $x + 21 = y$

In six years, he will be one-fifth of his mother's age. So we can assume that: $5 \times (x + 6) = y + 6$

Frome this equation we derive:

$5x + 6 = y + 6$

$y = 5x + 24$

We replace y in the first equation:

$x + 21 = 5x + 24$

$-3 = 4x$

$x = -3 \div 4 \text{ years} = -9 \text{ months}$

So the father must be very close to the mother!

21

Very close!

Solution for page 105

 PHINX

Man: in his infancy, he walks on all fours, as an adult, he stands up on two legs, and lastly, in his old age, he moves about with the help of a cane.

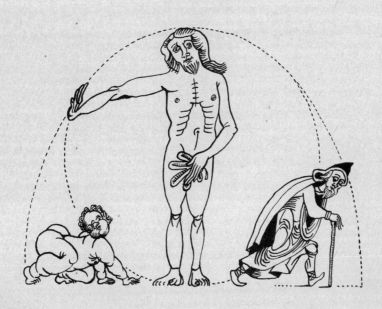

Solution for page 106

 HILDREN

The other half of his children are also daughters!

RSENIC

All the queen needs to do is to number the twelve boxes 1 to 12, from left to right. Then she must take:
- 1 pill from box 1
- 2 pills from box 2
- 3 pills from box 3
etc.
- 12 pills from box 12

Finally, she weighs all of the pills removed from the boxes, or 78 pills in all. If all of them were purely medicinal, they would weigh:

$$78 \times 10 = 780 \text{ oz}$$

Knowing that a pill of arsenic weighs 1 oz less, all she has to do is calculate the difference between 780 oz and the result. For example, if the queen finds 777 oz, it's box 3 (from which she took 3 pills) that contains the arsenic. It looks like the king's favourite's days are... numbered!

AGNETISM

You should place them in the form of a T.

If nothing happens, the magnet is the one forming the horizontal bar of the T.

If they attract or repel, the magnet is the one constituting the T's vertical bar.

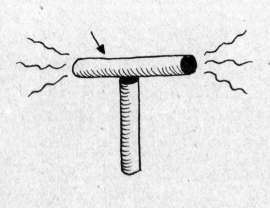

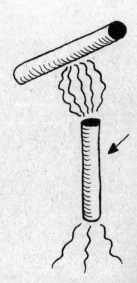

RIDGE CROSSING

First of all, A and B cross, which takes 2 minutes.

Then A brings back the torch, and 3 minutes have gone by.

C and D cross the bridge, and now 13 minutes have been used up.

B returns with the torch, and we're now at 15 minutes.

A and B cross the bridge, and 17 minutes have elapsed since the start. Quick, the ghoul is coming back!

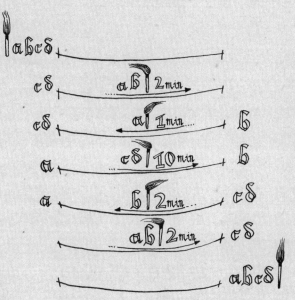

Solution for page 110

PASSWORD

The papal legate should reply, 'Five,' which corresponds to the number of letters in the number pronounced by the guard.

Solution for page 112

EHIND BARS

The prisoner, like most people, sees grey points between the squares. Yet they don't exist! Strange, isn't it?

 EAR

The circles seem to turn.
Don't you think that's odd?

Solution for page 114

HENS' EGGS

Two hundred eggs.

In fact, four hundred hens lay four hundred eggs in eight days.
Therefore four hundred hens lay two hundred eggs in four days.

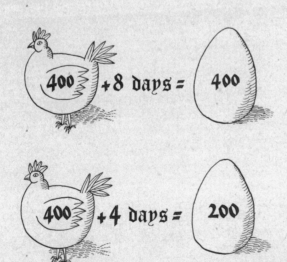

400 + 8 days = 400

400 + 4 days = 200

ATS

The same three cats!

If the three cats catch on average one mouse per minute, in one hundred minutes, they will catch one hundred mice.

Solution for page 117

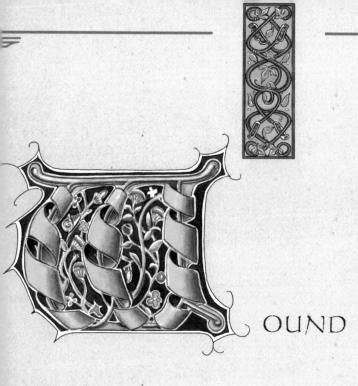

OUND

The doctor is his mother!

ULE DRIVER

He's on foot!

AIN COURTYARD

The figure representing the main courtyard is composed of thirty squares:

- sixteen of size 1 × 1;
- nine of size 2 × 2;
- four of size 3 × 3;
- and one of size 4 × 4.

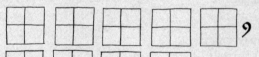

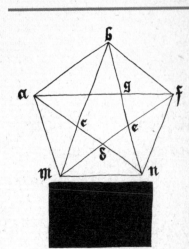

# OUNT THE TRIANGLES

There are two types of straight line here: those of the pentagon and those of the star. Let's start by considering those triangles having a side in common with the pentagon. For a given side NM, we can make six triangles (points A, B, C, D, E, and F).

If we apply this observation to the five sides in rotation, we see that certain triangles are counted twice: those which have two sides in common with the pentagon. If we exclude the triangle formed with point F (triangle NMF), there are no triangles counted twice. There are thus five triangles per side of the pentagon: twenty-five triangles are accounted for this way.

We have now dealt with all the cases of triangles having one side in common with the pentagon. The other triangles only have sides on the star. Consider the segment AN. Apart from triangles having sides in common with the pentagon, we can identify the triangles CDM and ANG. These are the only triangles possible without one side in common with the pentagon. Triangles of these two types are repeated five times in rotation around the figure. So we have ten more triangles here.

In all therefore, we have thirty-five triangles.

Solution for page 121

IVE ALIGNMENTS

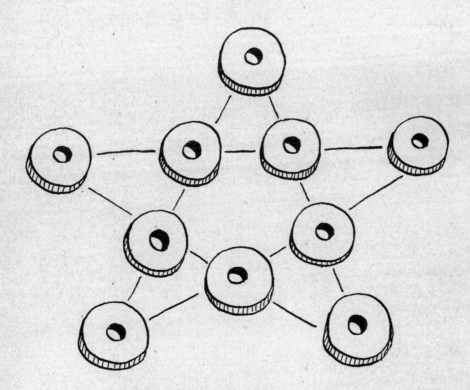

O YOUR QUILLS

You must trace the following path:
- from A to B,
- then the upper curve to E,
- then go to D,
- then the upper curve to C,
- then the straight line to D,
- then the lower curve to C,
- then the straight line to B,
- then the lower curve to E,
- then the straight line to F.

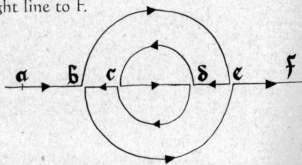

Solution for page 123

POWER TRANSFER

123**4**		
23**4**	1	
3**4**	1	2
3**4**		12
4	3	12
1**4**	3	2
1**4**	23	
4	123	
	123	**4**
	23	1**4**
2	3	1**4**
12	3	**4**
12		3**4**
2	1	3**4**
	1	23**4**
		123**4**

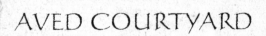

AVED COURTYARD

All the lines are perfectly straight.
Puzzling, isn't it?

OOL STOCKINGS

Since there three different colours, by taking four wool
stockings from her chest, Lady Brunehaut can be sure of having
a matched pair.

 HESTS

The bandits only need to glance into the chest bearing the label: 'gold and silver coins.' Indeed, since none of the labels are in their right place, this means that:
- if they see a gold coin, this chest can only contain gold coins,
- if they see a silver coin, this chest can only contain silver coins.
From this, they can deduce the contents of the two other chests.

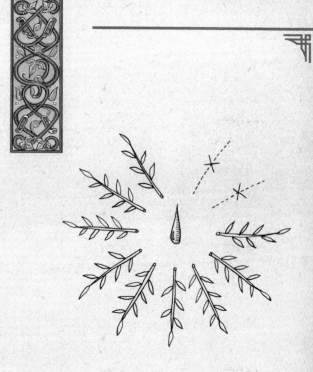

ELEVEN BRANCHES

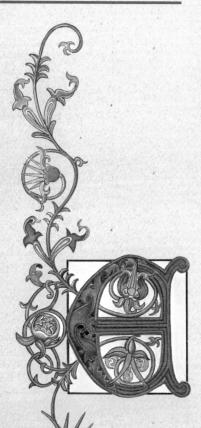

The solution is twofold:

Gawain takes two branches. The other knight can take one, two or three branches. In all these cases, Gawain will take three, two, or one branches, so as to collect the sixth (there will then remain five on the table).

From that point, when his rival takes one, two, or three branches, Gawain will gather up three, two, or one respectively, thus leaving the last one to the other knight.

 HEEP

The old shepherd lends a sheep to the three sons, which brings the number of sheep to eighteen.

Respecting the will of his old friend, he gives half to the eldest son, or nine sheep, a third to the middle son, six sheep, and a ninth to the last son, or two sheep.

This makes a total of $9 + 6 + 2 = 17$ sheep.

The terms of the will have been respected, and the old man can retrieve his sheep.

Solution for page 132

ALUE OF THE PRODUCT

The series is equal to 0 because (x - x) equals 0.

REAL NUMBERS ARE ALL POSITIVE?

The error is to be found in the passage from line 2 to line 3. The property cited is only true if x is positive or 0.

Solution for page 134

ALTERNATION

Just four moves.

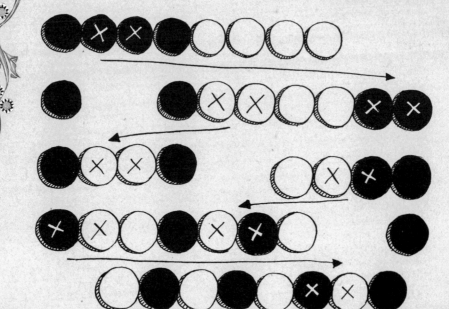

PURSES

You need to empty the contents of the second purse into the fifth and then replace the second, now empty, back in its original spot.

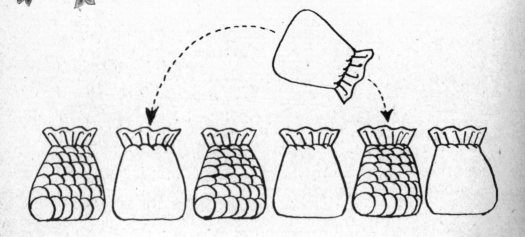

Solution for page 136

OW MUCH PROFIT?

The merchant has made a profit of 20 shillings.

He first earned 10 shillings by reselling for 80 shillings the cloth that he bought for 70, then 10 more by selling for 100 shillings the cloth that he acquired for 90.

Solution for page 137

A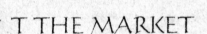 T THE MARKET

Let us assume that:

x = the amount that Lady Ermangarde had upon entering a shop.

y = the amount she had upon leaving the same shop.

The amount she spent (x - y) in the shop is therefore x ÷ 2 + 10, this can be expressed as

x - y = (x ÷ 2 + 10)

x - x ÷ 2 - 10 = y

x ÷ 2 - 10 = y

x ÷ 2 = y + 10

x = 2 × (y + 10)

This equation can be applied in each shop.

After the last shop, she has nothing left; so we can posit that y = 0:

2 × (0 + 10) = 20

She thus had 20 shillings upon entering the last shop. The same calculation applied to the preceding shops gives us:

2 × (20 + 10) = 60

2 × (60 + 10) = 140

2 × (140 + 10) = 300

2 × (300 + 10) = 620

She had 620 shillings at the start.

Solution for page 138

ECAPITATION

The two squires have lost their head… the king!

EMPTY GLASS

Only one, because after that, the goblet is no longer empty!

OUR CARDS AND FOUR
LETTERS

You need to turn over three cards. This will give three different cases:
- The G card.

You need to turn this over to see if there is an L on the back.
- The L card.

It is useless turning this card over. Whether the letter on the back is a G or not, it does not change matters.
- The D and P cards.

You need to turn these over. If one of these cards has a G on its back, the statement is false.

ARD BRAIN-TEASER

Thanks to clues 1 and 3, we know that the cards we seek are a king, a 5, and a 10.

It only remains to determine their suit and their place.

From clue 2, we can propose three hypotheses:

 This hypothesis is eliminated by clue 4.

 This hypothesis is eliminated by clue 3.

 This hypothesis is therefore the correct one.

Lastly, we know from clue 3 that the 10 is to the left of the heart, and from clue 1 that the 5 is to the right of the king.

The answer is therefore:

Solution for page 142

 USES

First of all, Merlin lights A, B, and C, at the same time.

When the first fuse (A B) is entirely consumed, 30 minutes will have gone by. Merlin will then light D...

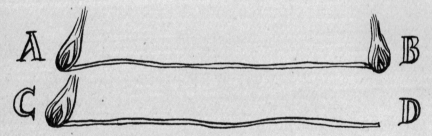

... and the 30 minutes of fuse (C D) remaining will be consumed in 15 minutes.

30 min + 15 min = 45 min.

Solution for page 144

PADLOCK

After having placed the locks of her hair in the box, Isolde must secure it with her padlock and send it to Tristan. Upon receiving the box, he will add his own padlock and send it back to her. Isolde receives the box, removes the padlock belonging to her, and sends it once again to her lover, who upon receipt can now remove his padlock and find the celebrated love token.

RAGONFLY

The lovers, advancing at the same speed, each travel 50 furlongs at a speed of 10 furlongs per hour. They therefore meet at the end of 5 hours.

So, the dragonfly will have flown:

$5 \times 150 = 750$ furlongs.

Solution for page 146

 ALINDROME

The next palindrome is 16061.

The knight thus travels 110 furlongs in 2 hours, which means that he rides at a speed of 55 furlongs per hour.

 UINEVERE

Starting from any point on the circumference of the tower, the queen first of all headed north until she reached another point on the tower's circumference. Then she turned 90° to the west until she ran into the wall again.

Her trajectory corresponds to the two shorter sides of a right-angled triangle, measuring respectively 30 and 40 paces.

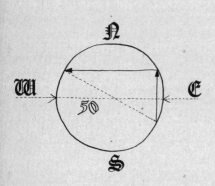

Now, the hypotenuse of a right-angled triangle inscribed in a circle coincides with its diameter.

Knowing that the square of the hypotenuse of a right-angled triangle is equal to the sum of the squares of the other two sides, we have:

$$\text{hypotenuse}^2 = 30^2 + 40^2$$
$$\text{hypotenuse}^2 = 900 + 1600 = 2500$$
$$\text{hypotenuse} = \sqrt{2500} = 50$$

The tower has a diameter of 50 paces.

ATER LILY

It would take nine years.

Since each water lily doubles in surface area each year, the water lily that will completely cover the pond in the tenth year therefore covers half of it in the ninth year. The second water lily also covers half, so together they cover it completely.

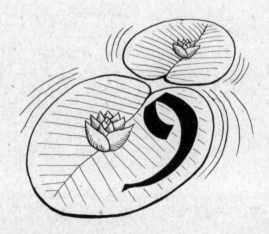

 IRD BECOMES DRAGON

It is possible to convert all of the birds in the enclosure into dragons in just four steps:

Step 1 - Open lock 2

Step 4 - Open lock 4.

Steps 2 and 3 -
Open locks 5 and 8.

Solution for page 150

 LIMBING SNAIL

It reaches the top of the wall on the evening of the eighth day:

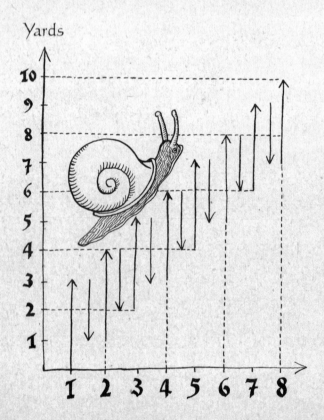

Solution for page 152

EAR HUNT

The bear is white. In fact, this phenomenon is only possible at the following places:

1. Exactly at the North Pole.

The 5 miles to the east are not straight in line: the route forms the arc of a circle while remaining at a distance of 5 miles from the pole (at each instant, one is moving eastwards). The bear is a polar bear, so it is white.

2. Let us imagine a latitude where it is possible to go around the world in 5 miles. These exist very near the South Pole and the North Pole. Near the North Pole, the hunter would be less than 5 miles from the pole, so it would not be possible to arrive there after travelling 10 km to the south. So let's look at the vicinity of the South Pole.

Consider a circle, parallel to the equator (that is to say, a circle of latitude), with a circumference of 5 miles, which goes around the world at this very location. We depart from a point located 5 miles to the north of this circle. We travel 5 miles south (so we find ourselves on this circle), 5 miles east (we go around the world and find ourselves back at the preceding position), then 5 miles north (we find ourselves back at the starting point).

The second solution is therefore: all the points located on a circle 5 miles to the north of a second circle 5 miles in circumference, in the Southern hemisphere. But as we all know, there aren't any bears, polar or otherwise, living in the Antarctic…

Solution for page 153

IGITAL DISPLAY

In the course of a day, the display goes from 0:00 to 23:59.
Twelve hours of the day contain the number 1:

1:00	13:00	17:00
10:00	14:00	18:00
11:00	15:00	19:00
12:00	16:00	21:00

Moreover, in the course of the same hour, the number 1
appears fifteen times at the following minutes:

hr:01	hr:16	hr:51
hr:10	hr:17	
hr:11	hr:18	
hr:12	hr:19	
hr:13	hr:21	
hr:14	hr:31	
hr:15	hr:41	

Therefore, for a 24-hour day this gives us:

$24 \times 15 = 360$ occurrences

$360 + 12 = 372$

In all, the number 1 thus appears 372 times in the course
of a day.

Solution for page 154

URVEYOR

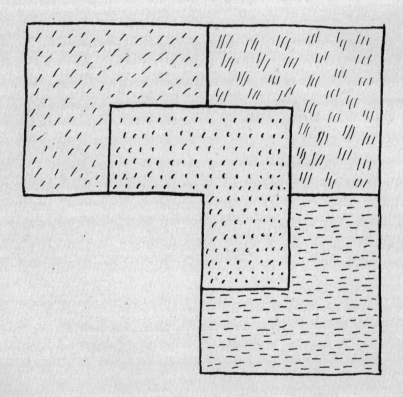

PRISON

 T THE INN

The problem lies in the final sum: 27 + 2 = 29

At the end of the exchanges, the distribution is the following:

- Innkeeper: 27 pence, of which:
  Price of the room: 25 pence
  Tip: 2 pence
- Rag trader: 1 penny
- Draper: 1 penny
- Tapestry-maker: 1 penny

Nothing is lost.

The two pennies in the sum 27 + 2 = 29 are already part of the 27.

27 (of which 2 [tip] and 25 [room]) + 3 [clients] = 30 [total]

or again:

30 [total] - 3 [clients] - 2 [tip] = 25 [room]

All is well!

DEAFNESS

The abbot should proceed as follows:

• he must tell the first monk to give the signal to light the candle, wait 2 minutes then ask him to give another signal to extinguish the candle;

• he must then tell the second monk to give the signal to light the candle, and go up himself to check on things in the chapel:

  - if the candle is lit, Friar Benedict heard the second monk,

  - if the candle is out, but the abbot can see a little melted wax, Friar Benedict heard the first monk,

  - if the candle is out and cold, this means that Friar Benedict can only hear the third monk.

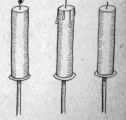

Solution for page 158

 WO GUARDS

He must ask one of the two guards:
'Which door will the other guard tell me is the door leading
to the exit?'
Then all he has to do is to choose the opposite door.

Solution for page 159

UCKY DRAW

The prisoner needs to draw one of the marbles at random and swallow it without looking at it. Then, the only way of knowing which marble he drew will be to look at the marble remaining in the helmet, which will of course be black.

The king, in the presence of his people, will have to resign himself to freeing the prisoner.

Solution for page 160

OME MENTAL CALCULATIONS

$$2 + 2 - 2 - 2 = 0$$
$$(2 \div 2) \times (2 \div 2) = 1$$
$$(2 \div 2) + (2 \div 2) = 2$$
$$(2 + 2 + 2) \div 2 = 3$$
$$2 + 2 + 2 - 2 = 4$$
$$2 + 2 + (2 \div 2) = 5$$
$$(2 \times 2 \times 2) - 2 = 6$$
$$(2 \times 2 \times 2) + 2 = 10$$
$$(2 + 2 + 2) \times 2 = 12$$

$$(3 + 3 + 3) \div 3 = 3$$
$$((3 \times 3) + 3) \div 3 = 4$$
$$3 + 3 - (3 \div 3) = 5$$
$$3 + 3 + 3 - 3 = 6$$
$$3 + 3 + (3 \div 3) = 7$$
$$(3 \times 3) - (3 \div 3) = 8$$
$$(3 \times 3) + 3 - 3 = 9$$
$$(3 \times 3) + (3 \div 3) = 10$$

$$((4 \times 4) - 4) \div 4 = 3$$
$$((4 + 4) \div 4) + 4 = 6$$
$$4 + 4 - (4 \div 4) = 7$$
$$(4 \times 4) - 4 - 4 = 8$$
$$(4 \times 4) + 4 + 4 = 24$$
$$(4 \times 4) \times 4 - 4 = 28$$
$$(4 \times 4) + (4 \times 4) = 32$$
$$(4 + 4 + 4) \times 4 = 48$$

$$(5 + 5 + 5) \div 5 = 3$$
$$((5 - 5) \times 5) + 5 = 5$$
$$((5 \times 5) + 5) \div 5 = 6$$
$$(5 \times 5) + (5 \div 5) = 26$$
$$(5 + (5 : 5)) \times 5 = 30$$
$$(5 \times 5) + (5 \times 5) = 50$$
$$((5 + 5) \times 5) + 5 = 55$$
$$(5 \times 5 \times 5) - 5 = 120$$

Solution for page 161

DDITION

$$8 + 8 + 8 + 88 + 888 = 1000$$

29 FEBRUARY

He will be 28 years old.

Every year the same date in the same month will fall a day later in the week, because 365 is a multiple of 7 plus 1.
In leap years, which have 366 days, it falls two days later.
Leap years occur every four years.
Between two February 29s, there is therefore a difference of five days (3 + 2).
So the first 29 February after the birth of a child will fall five days later, on a Saturday.

The second will fall on a Thursday, third on a Tuesday, the fourth on a Sunday, the fifth on a Friday, the sixth on a Wednesday, and finally the seventh on a Monday.

Lady Gertrude's son will thus be 7 × 4 = 28 years old the next time his birthday falls on a Monday.

UMBER OF DAYS

From January 1008 to December 1012, five years have gone by, that is, 5 × 12 = 60 months.

During this period, there are sixty months with twenty-eight days, since every month has at least twenty-eight days!

60

Solution for page 164

IVE TRIANGLES

We get: 1 big triangle + 4 small triangles = 5 triangles.

Solution for page 165

ATCHES 3

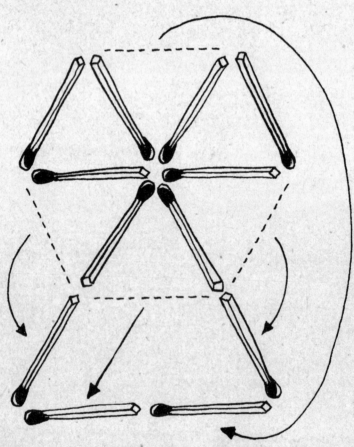

Solution for page 166

UNIVERSITY

The answer is 'nothing.'
Nothing is better than God.
Nothing is worse than the Devil.
The poor have nothing.
The rich need nothing.
And if you eat nothing, you die.

NOTHING

Solution for page 167

 HADOW OF THE TOWER

None; square A is the same shade as square B.
   Perplexing, isn't it?

 ABRIC CLIPPING

Never! The diagonal lines are parallel, and therefore they can never meet. Do you find that disorientating?

OWER OF COINS

Label the five stacks as A, B, C, D, and E.

The nine successive manoeuvres should start, in order, from the following stacks: A, B, C, D, E, D, C, B, A.

Solution for page 170

AGIC SQUARE

There are two possible answers:

LICES OF CAKE

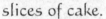

Two solutions are possible:
 - either one of the three knife strokes can be made horizontally through the cake;
 - or the cook can first cut the cake in two and then put one half on top of the other. Next, he cuts his cake again and obtains four slices. Superimposing the four slices a final time, he cuts them in half and obtains eight identical slices of cake.

Solution for page 172

PANCAKES

The baker must bake three pancakes, each with two sides, which we will call a and b.

The quickest way to bake the three pancakes is as follows.

step 1: pancake 1 side a, and pancake 2 side a

step 2: pancake 2 side b, and pancake 3 side a

step 3: pancake 1 side b, and pancake 3 side b

With each step lasting 3 minutes, it will take 9 minutes for the baker to bake the three pancakes.

Note: other solutions exist, all involving the same number of steps.

Solution for page 173

HAT DAY?

Sunday

Solution for page 176

STRANGE DATE

This date can be written in the form of a palindrome, meaning it can be read the same forwards or backwards:

29/11/1192 or 2911/11/92

Solution for page 177

ITTLE RECTANGLE BECOMES SQUARE

The area of the rectangular parchment is 2 ($l \times L = 2 \times 1 = 2$). Therefore each side of the square must be the root of 2.

The parchment is therefore cut so that we get four segments whose longest side is root 2.

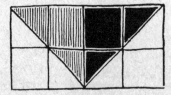

They are rearranged like this:

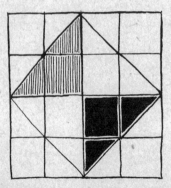

And the rectangle becomes a square!

Solution for page 178

ONG RECTANGLE BECOMES SQUARE

The area of the rectangle formed by the parchment is 5 (w × L = 5 × 1 = 1). Therefore the side of the square must be $\sqrt{5}$.

So the parchment is cut up in a way to make the straight segments with a length of $\sqrt{5}$ appear:

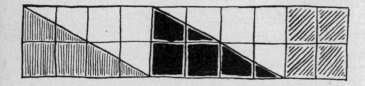

They can be rearranged like this:

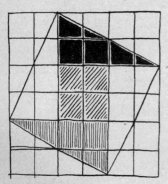

And the long rectangle is transformed into a square!

Solution for page 179

 LLEGIANCE

There are only three combinations of truth and falsehood, shown below. Only the third combination is possible and therefore both are lying, which means that Sir Thomas serves King Richard and Sir Robert serves Prince John.

If...		Then...		Possible
Sir Thomas says	Sir Robert says	Sir Thomas serves	Sir Robert serves	
True	False	Prince John	Prince John	No
False	True	King Richard	King Richard	No
False	False	King Richard	Prince John	Yes

 ERFS

Only one of these assertions is true. If Lady Margaret's assertion is true, then that of her daughter is also true, which is impossible, since we know that only one statement is true.

There remains Eudes's claim, but if it is true that there are any serfs working the land at all, then that of his sister is also true, which is still impossible. Therefore there are no serfs working on the duke of Burgundy's land.

No serfs!

CASUALTIES OF WAR

30% have both eyes,
25% have both ears,
20% have both arms
and 15% have two legs.

So at least 90% are not suffering from all four handicaps.
That makes a minimum of 10% who are missing at the same time
an eye, an ear, an arm, and a leg all at the same time.

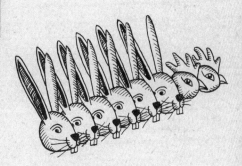

ABBIT FEET

Let x be the number of chickens and y the number of rabbits.

The number of heads is therefore x + y and equals 8.

The number of feet is therefore 2x + 4y and equals 28.

Therefore:

[1] $x + y = 8$

[2] $2x + 4y = 28$

Equation [1] gives us: $x = 8 - y$ [3]

If we use this to replace x in [2], we get:

$2(8 - y) + 4y = 28$

$16 - 2y + 4y = 28$

$2y = 12$

$y = 6$

From equation [3], we get:

$x = 2$

Landry has two chickens and six rabbits.

PROHIBITION

Strangely, most people don't see the repetition of the word 'AT.'

Solution for page 184

 FFF

This text has six F's.
Most people forget the F's in 'OF.' What about you?

HISKY

This sentence uses all twenty-six letters of the alphabet.

26

>alphabet<

 OGICAL SERIES 4

Each term in this series corresponds to the number of letters comprising the name of the preceding number ('five' has four letters, 'four' has four letters...)

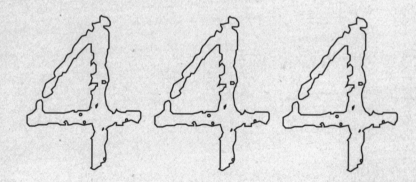

Solution for page 187

ARAB NUMERAL EQUATION

The + becomes a 4.

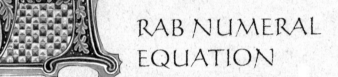

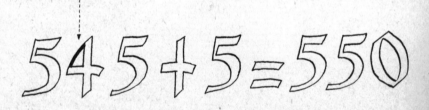

WATCHTOWER

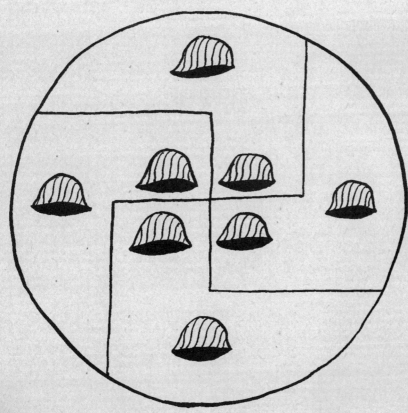

STRAIGHT LINES

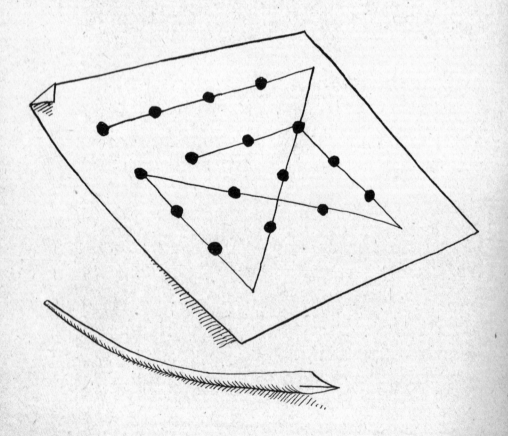

Solution for page 190

HE WORM IN THE MANUSCRIPT

The worm will have travelled 40½ inches, not 49½ inches.

The first page of volume I and the last page of volume X are not at the extremities of the set of books.

If you have trouble seeing this, take a book after having determined the location of the first page and place it upright on your bookshelf. You may be surprised!

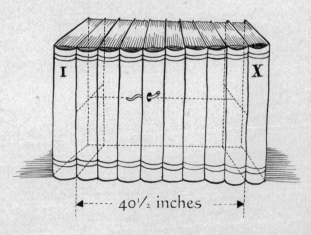

40½ inches

EETING

Since they meet, the two groups of monks will obviously both be at the same distance from Cluny at the moment of their meeting!

Solution for page 192

 OGICAL SERIES 5

You only need to write down what you read:
One 1: 11
Two 1: 21
One two, one 1: 1211
One 1, one 2, two 1: 111221
Three 1, two 2, one 1: 312211

The next number is therefore:
One 3, one 1, two 2, two 1: 13112221

13112221

Solution for page 193

O 4 IN THE SERIES

Let us suppose that a 4 does appear in a line. This 4 must necessarily have a character to its right (only 1s can end lines). Let us call it x.
Line [I] will thus have 4 consecutive x's:

[I]   ....
[II]   ....axxxxb
[III] .....4x........

Now, we can break each line down into pairs, first a quantifier (which defines how many figure x's there are) and then a quantified number (the figure x which was found on the preceding line).

We can thus read line [II] in two ways: either a is the quantified number (hypothesis 1), or it is the quantifier (hypothesis 2).
Ine the first case, a is the quantified number; the breakdown into pairs is as follows:
[II] ... a xx xx b...
Line [I] would therefore be:
x in x occurrences then x in x occurrences
[I] ... xxxxxxx xxxxxxx...

      x times   x times

But that is impossible because then we would read line [II] like this

[II] ... a(2x)xb...

That is not true, so the hypothesis is false.

In the second case, a is the quantifier; the breakdown into pairs is as follows:

[II] ...ax xx xb

Line [I] will thus be:

x in a occurrences then x in x occurrences and lastly b in x occurrences

[I] ...xxxxxxx xxxxxx bbbbbbbb...

      a times   x times

= Once again, in this case, line [II] would read: [II] ...(a + x)x + xb...

That is not true, so the hypothesis is false as with any number higher than 3.

 ISHING

In fact there are three people who go fishing, not four: grandfather, father and the latter's son - who constitute two fathers accompanied by their sons.

 ART

Who said it was night-time?

NIGHT!

Solution for page 196

N THE PURSE

One of the coins is not a 10-groat piece, but the other one is! So the monkey thief's purse contains a 20-groat coin and a 10-groat coin.

Solution for page 197

 HAIN

The trick consists in breaking the three links of the same piece of chain, which will cost 15 sovereigns.

Then with three solderings, the other three pieces are linked together, which will cost 30 sovereigns. In all, Sir Godfrey will have spent 45 sovereigns.

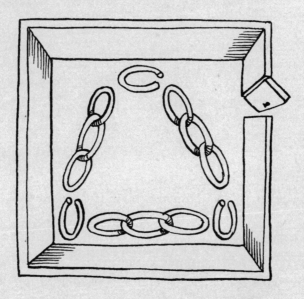

HREE-WAY GAME

Since 9 is an odd number, Eberulf must have lost the last round. Before that round, their holdings were: 4 / 18 / 5 (round no. 5)

Same method for the preceding rounds:

Leander lost round no. 4, when each of them started with:

2 shillings (Martin), 9 shillings (Eberulf), and 16 shillings (Leander).

Eberulf lost round no. 3, when each of them started with:

1 shilling (Martin), 18 shillings (Eberulf), and 8 shillings (Leander).

Martin lost round no. 2, when each of them started with:

14 shillings (Martin), 9 shillings (Eberulf), and 4 shillings (Leander).

Eberulf lost round no. 1, when each of them started with: 7 shillings (Martin), 18 shillings (Eberulf), and 2 shillings (Leander).

NKWELL

Let x be the cost of the quill.

The cost of the inkwell equals $x + 10$

The sum of the two objects equals $x + x + 10 = 11$

Therefore $2x + 10 = 11$

$2x = 11 - 10 = 1$

$x = 1 \div 2 = 0.5$

The quill thus costs half a shilling and the inkwell ten and a half shillings.

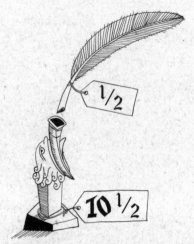

 EAPFROG

You need a minimum of fifteen moves to reverse
the order of the pieces in this configuration.

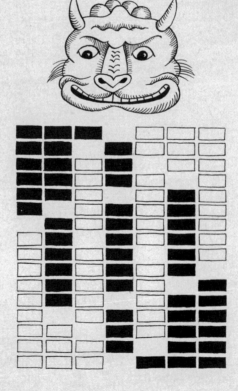

ATHEDRAL

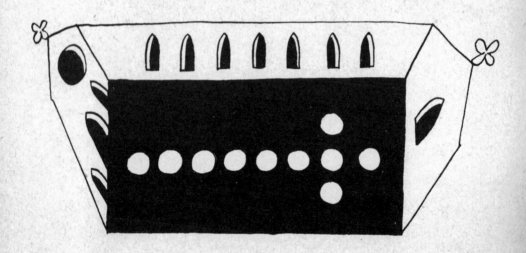

UELS

Since each duel eliminates a knight and there only remains one at the end, the number of duels is n - 1.

$$n-1$$

WO BROTHERS

From the first to the twelfth tower there are eleven intervals
(12 - 1 = 11), while from the twelfth to the twenty-fourth
tower there are twelve intervals (24 - 12 = 12). Peter thus had
a shorter course.

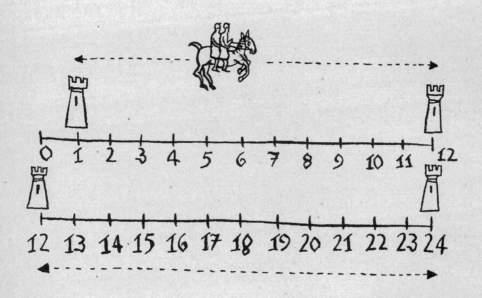

HREE DAUGHTERS

Here are the prime factors of 36:

3 × 3 × 2 × 2

So the possible combinations are:

- 36, 1, 1 → the sum of which is equal to 38.
- 18, 2, 1 → the sum of which is equal to 21.
- 12, 3, 1 → the sum of which is equal to 16.
- 9, 4, 1 → the sum of which is equal to 14.
- 9, 2, 2 → the sum of which is equal to 13.
- 6, 6, 1 → the sum of which is equal to 13.
- 6, 3, 2 → the sum of which is equal to 11.
- 4, 3, 3 → the sum of which is equal to 10.

Unlike us, the peasant woman knows the number of eggs that her acquaintance has in her basket. And if this number was 38 or 11, for example, she would announce the solution right away; if she hasn't found it, it's because it involves the only uncertain case: 13.
So the ages are either (6, 6, 1) or (9, 2, 2).

Of these two configurations, only (9, 2, 2) has a single eldest daughter, the other has eldest twins. The eldest daughter must thus be nine years old, while the twins are two.

OSEBUSH

The rose bush measures 60 ins (30 ins + half of 60 ins, or 30 ins).

 ANDLES

Four.

With nine candle stubs, he makes three new ones, which will be lit. From these three new candles, there will remain three stubs, which will allow him to reconstitute a fourth candle.

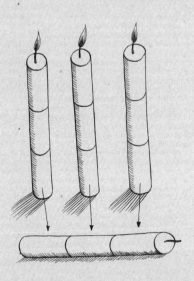

Solution for page 207

 IRE

The king gives his men the order to halt and start a fire in front of them. Thanks to the wind blowing at 50 miles per hour, the fire will propagate itself forward more rapidly than the troops will advance.

It only remains for Louis IX to signal his troops to resume their march. They will then make their way without danger and faster over the area that has already burned.

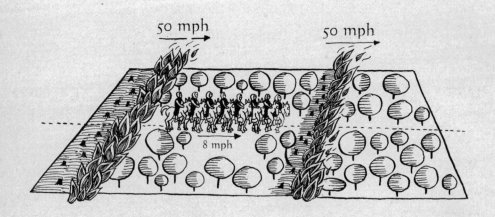

50 mph

50 mph

8 mph

 EVERSIBLE
TRIANGLE

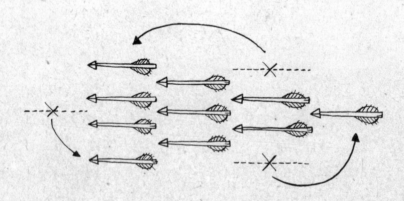

ROSE WINDOW

Neither, the two circles have the same diameter.
Unusual, isn't it?

 OGICAL SERIES 6

The first spaces are occupied by the numbers 1 to 7, side-by-side with their mirror images.

The missing symbols are therefore:

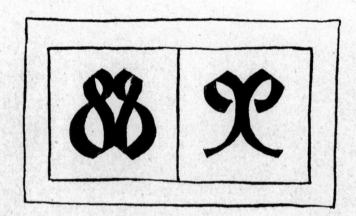

 ATHER AND SON

A figure double of the year in progress.

ORTURE

Say this: 'I will be quartered!'

The torturer will find himself faced with this paradox: if he quarters you, your assertion will be true, so he will have to burn you alive.

And if he burns you alive, your assertion will be false. Since he will not be able to find a way of putting you to death without repudiating his promise, with a little luck, he will let you go!

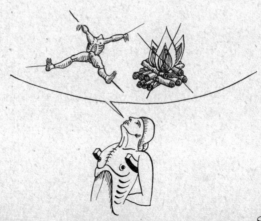

Solution for page 214

 ANCE

The knight bought a rectangular case measuring four feet by three. The diagonal of the case, equal to the length of the lance, corresponds to the hypotenuse of a right-angled triangle whose other two sides are the Length (L) and width (w) of the case. Reminder: the square of the hypotenuse of a right-angled triangle is equal to the sum of the squares of the two sides.

Here: $L^2 + w^2 = 5^2 = 25$

$4^2 + 3^2 = 5$

$L = 4$

$w = 3$

The length of the case being equal to four feet, the guard can no longer deny entry to the knight.

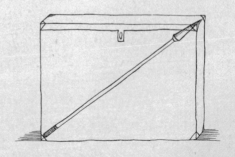

STAIRCASE

If they join forces, it would take two weeks for the two architects to finish the staircase, the Florentine architect building a third of the staircase while his Flemish colleague builds the remaining two thirds.

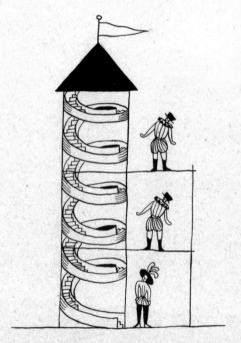

Solution for page 216

MILLION HAIRS

The answer is yes. If the number of inhabitants is greater than the maximum number of hairs on anyone's head, then there must be an insufficient number of 'hairs on head' for all of them to have a different number. Certain inhabitants of the kingdom of France must necessarily have the same numbers of hairs on their head.

And what about fleas?

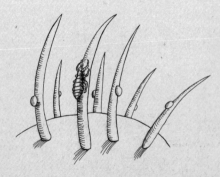

Solution for page 217

HREE SWISS

The three Swiss are... women!

Solution for page 218

UE SOUTH HOUSE

The house is located at the North Pole!

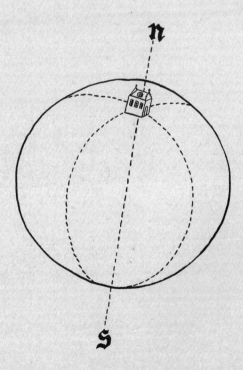

ASTIME

He turns over the two hourglasses, until the little one is empty, at 4 minutes.

He turns over the little one and lets it run down until the big one is empty, at 7 minutes.

He turns over the big one and lets it run down until the little one is empty. 8 minutes have gone by.

Lastly, he turns over the big one and waits for it to empty. He can then take his sauce off the fire, because the 9 minutes are up.

Solution for page 220

OUR PUZZLE NOTES

OUR PUZZLE NOTES

OUR PUZZLE NOTES

OUR PUZZLE NOTES

OUR PUZZLE NOTES

OUR PUZZLE NOTES

OUR PUZZLE NOTES

OUR PUZZLE NOTES

OUR PUZZLE NOTES

OUR PUZZLE NOTES

OUR PUZZLE NOTES

OUR PUZZLE NOTES